INSECT FACT
AND FOLKLORE

THE MACMILLAN COMPANY
NEW YORK · CHICAGO
DALLAS · ATLANTA · SAN FRANCISCO

THE MACMILLAN COMPANY
OF CANADA, LIMITED
TORONTO

INSECT FACT
AND FOLKLORE

Lucy W. Clausen, Ph.D.

The American Museum of Natural History
(Department of Public Instruction)

and

Columbia University
(College of Pharmacy)

New York 1954
THE MACMILLAN COMPANY

To:

Mother
and
Father

Preface

Insects are endlessly fascinating, although most laymen consider them nuisances and pests. Unquestionably, a minority are, and man must battle incessantly to keep them under control. But though these are bothersome, they are not less alluring to those who study them.

The lives, the habits, the structure of all insects reveal their inherent ingenuity and beauty. Insects have always been part of man's life, and the many folk tales from all parts of the world reflect his original attitude of friendliness toward them. The uses of insects in industry show that some kinds rank with the world's important plant crops.

It was not until I pointed up such facts by narrating stories in lectures that I began to strike a responsive chord in my audiences. Then, in searching literature for further topics pertaining to insect folklore, products, uses, and other less known associations with man, I soon became aware that this widely scattered information had never been brought together in one volume. I have therefore tried to assemble it here against just enough of a background of scientific detail, such as classification and nomenclature, to enable the reader to find his way later through the standard texts and reference works.

Texts on entomology, like most lectures and classroom studies, as well as those books in which the science is popularized, follow more or less the same pattern in presenting technical details. This book is thus a departure from the usual volume on insects. Of necessity, it lacks a certain amount of continuity, because entomology here, instead of being the sole subject treated, serves as the core of a study which is largely concerned with anthropology.

Presenting insects in a favorable light has been a concern of mine as far back as I can remember. In continuing my aim in this book

I have attempted: (a) to bring together nontechnical information on insects which would not otherwise be readily available; (b) to provide a comprehensive bibliography giving the sources of this material; and (c), most important of all, to initiate the layman into the subject of entomology by interlacing elementary scientific data with stories of more popular interest having insects as the common element.

The book is devoted mainly to the better known forms of insects, to those which play important roles in the customs of peoples throughout the world, and to insects which, because of their products, have been the basis for various industries. At the end, I have included some of the insects whose ravages have made them the enemies of mankind, showing the recent progress of scientists in conquering them.

It is my hope that this book will instill a sympathetic understanding through which people will overcome their natural (though unreasonable) aversion to insects. Further, I hope that my work will arouse some of the readers to undertake more serious adventures into the rewarding field of entomology.

Here I wish to make grateful acknowledgment of my indebtedness to the following persons:

To Dr. George Gaylord Simpson of The American Museum of Natural History for a critical reading of the original manuscript which resulted in a complete revision and rearrangement of the text;

to Dr. James A. Forbes of Fordham University for checking on scientific accuracy and for constructive criticisms;

to Dr. Charles Tanzer of the Board of Education of the City of New York for a critical reading from the layman's point of view;

to Mrs. Jan B. Fairservis, Staff Artist in the Department of Exhibition at The American Museum of Natural History, for her beautiful illustrations and an interest far exceeding contractual obligation,

and to Mr. Louis A. Monaco of The American Museum of Natural History for his collaboration during preparation of the manuscript.

However, the responsibility for any shortcomings in this volume rests entirely upon my own shoulders.

Lucy W. Clausen.

New York
March, 1954.

Table of Contents

Illustrations

Chapter I

Insects Everywhere!

In recent years more than ever before, man has come to realize that insects, for good or bad, are his constant companions in nearly every aspect of life. The men who fought in tropical areas became familiar with insects that bite and sting and those that transmit human diseases. The thousands of new gardeners have been appalled at the numbers of small voracious creatures that feed upon their plants. Increasing travel has emphasized the omnipresence and variety of insects. Research continually directs further attention to insects and their potential for benefit or evil.

Of all classes of animals, insects are the only creatures that have adapted themselves to every climatic and topographical condition. They can be seen almost everywhere, crawling, creeping, and flying, up to altitudes exceeding 15,000 feet, from the north polar regions to some of the bleak islands off Cape Horn; on snow-clad mountains and glaciers, in hot springs, in fresh and brackish waters, and even in caves where the light of day never penetrates.

Insects play such an important part in the economy of nature and in everyday experience that they have affected the welfare and the folklore of peoples all over the world. In spite of the constant conflict of some insects with man, others are of direct advantage.

HOW TO DETERMINE AN INSECT

It is easy to determine an insect. All insects have six jointed legs and a body that is divided into three parts—a head, a thorax, and an abdomen. The head bears antennae, eyes, and mouthparts; the thorax is the *middle* section to which legs and wings (if wings are present) are attached; the abdomen bears the genitalia.

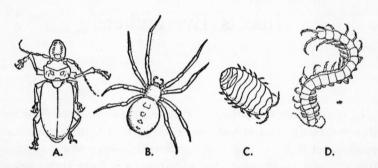

FIGURE 1.   An Insect and Some of its Close Relatives   All animals belonging to the Phylum Arthropoda are characterized by having sectioned body parts and paired jointed appendages.

   A. A beetle—a true insect.   All insects have *three pairs* of jointed legs.
   B. A spider—not an insect.   All spiders have *four pairs* of jointed legs.
   C. A crustacean—not an insect.   (A sow bug is illustrated.)   All crustaceans have *at least five pairs* of jointed legs and a varying number of supplementary legs attached to the lower abdominal segments.
   D. A centipede—not an insect.   Centipedes have one pair of jointed legs on each segment of the body, with the exception of the first and last segments—which have none.   A centipede may have from 13 to 95 *pairs* of legs.   Some tropical centipedes actually measure over a foot in length!

The number of legs as noted above are characteristic of the *adults* since they do vary in some species while immature.

Many of the small insectlike creatures that are commonly seen are not insects. For instance, spiders, scorpions, mites, and ticks are not insects. Though some have six legs in their immature stage these all have eight legs *when mature*. Moreover, none have bodies divided into three parts as do the true insects.

SIZE AND ABUNDANCE

In point of size, insects present a wide variation. They range from the smallest, much smaller than the head of an ordinary straight pin, to the giants in the insect kingdom—the bulky Goliath beetle of Africa which attains a length of over six inches, the walking stick of the Malay Peninsula which has been known to reach a length of thirteen inches, and an Australian moth known locally as the Hercules or Atlas moth, with a wingspread of fourteen inches. These giants are exceptions, for on the whole insects are small compared with mammals. In spite of their generally small size, some insects such as the army ants have the power for great destruction when a huge "army" is on the march. Then their ferocity causes birds and small mammals and even man to flee before them.

And consider the thoroughness of a mass attack by locusts (shorthorned grasshoppers) which have been known to fly in such countless numbers that they obscured the sun, turning the day into night for hours at a time. At such times they eat every living green thing over large areas, so that even mammals die from starvation. As recently as July 17, 1945, a news report from Chungking, China, stated that "Pan Lien-Yu, councillor from Shansi, reported that locusts had eaten the entire wheat crop in twenty districts of northeast Shansi, leaving 6,000,000 persons starving. . . ."

Insects have developed an incredible abundance of species, far in excess of the other animals on this earth. There are actually more than half a million named species of insects, and countless numbers of others still await identification and classification, in spite of the fact that they are being scientifically named and described in print at the rate of about ten thousand yearly.

Among the factors which contribute to the numerical predominance of insects are the great numbers of eggs (or young) in a family, and the rapidity with which generations succeed each other. In the case of the housefly, for example, both factors cooperate to produce an increase of flies as summer approaches. This increase would reach catastrophic proportions if it were not for the continually operating factors of natural control. According to Hodge, "A pair of flies beginning operations in April, might be the progenitors, if all were to live, of 191,010,000,000,000,000,000 flies by August. Allowing ⅛ cubic inch to a fly, this number would cover the earth 47 feet deep."

Many biologists have been struck by the remarkable disparity between the numbers of insects which are mathematically possible and the very tiny proportion of that number which actually come into existence. While the progeny from one fertile pair of insects might, theoretically, reach one hundred million within a year, perhaps only a hundred may survive. Therefore, the one hundred million never exist, except on paper, because they could have existed only had there been no juvenile mortality in earlier generations. The mortality necessary to maintain an insect population at a steady level is not difficult to calculate: If an insect lay ₁ one hundred eggs, a 98 per cent mortality in each generation would keep the population at the existing level, whereas with two hundred eggs per generation a 99 per cent mortality is necessary. To go further: If a pair of insects produces one hundred fertilized eggs, 98 of the resulting progeny must die before they reach the stage of egg-laying, in order to have a steady population. If, owing to more favorable conditions, only 96 die, then the size of the population will double in a single generation. If 99 die, the population will be halved. Thus, because of the high birth rate typical of insects, a very small percentage change in the death rate may produce very great changes in total insect populations.

In its natural or original habitat, a species of insect is ordinarily maintained in a state of equilibrium by the interaction upon it of biological and environmental agencies. If, however, any factor or set of factors disturbs this natural balance, the species may be able to achieve a supernormal ascendency for a variable period of time. For example, if such a species finds a home in a foreign country in which it experiences a favorable environment where those agencies which control it in its normal habitat are ineffective or wanting, the stage is set for that species to multiply and spread and even, as in the case of the gypsy moth, assume the status of a pest.

PERPETUATION OF SPECIES

The first stage of an insect is an egg. Eggs may sometimes be developed within the body of the mother; then again, they may be laid singly or in masses. Among termites, ants, and bees, a single individual may lay thousands of eggs over a period of many years. The size of the eggs varies from an almost microscopic dimension about $\frac{1}{250}$th of an inch in length, to globular forms about $\frac{1}{4}$ of an inch in diameter.

The places in which insects deposit their eggs vary according to species. Eggs may be dropped at random over grassy areas or laid on living hosts, on leaves or bark, in dung or decaying vegetation. They may also be inserted beneath the soil or into plant or animal tissues. The adult females usually deposit their eggs in locations where the immediate food needs of their offspring will be available. This is true even when the nutrition required by the young hatching from these eggs is entirely different from the food needs of the adult.

While perpetuation of insects is normally dependent upon the meeting of the sexes for fertilization of the eggs, different species reproduce in many exceptional ways. Here may be found reproduction without the act of mating (parthenogenesis); the production of living young (viviparity); production of offspring by the immature insect in the larval or in the pupal stage (paedogenesis), and production of two or more embryos from a single egg by a process of budding (polyembryony). Budding occurs among certain parasitic insects when one fertilized egg divides and then each division redivides, until well over one hundred identical individuals may result from the one original fertilized egg.

Immediately upon hatching (or birth) from the egg, insects undergo a series of remarkable changes in form. A nectar-sucking, winged butterfly was first a leaf-eating caterpillar; a bee originally lived the life of a clumsy, footless grub; and flies, which are so graceful and active, developed from maggots. The developing insect sheds and replaces its skin at various intervals. These changes are collectively termed *metamorphosis* and the young undergoing metamorphosis are called *larvae*. It is during this larval stage that all energy is directed toward eating. The farmer and the gardener are the hardest hit by such voracious appetites, since insect pests are estimated to devour or ruin about 10 per cent of all crops.

However, this loss is as nothing compared with crops which could not be produced without pollination. Among our flowering plants 85 per cent depend upon insects for the setting of fruit and the production of seed. If all insects were destroyed, there would not be such fruits as Smyrna figs, apples, pears, peaches, cherries, plums, or strawberries; and among the vegetable crops, cabbage, cauliflower, kale, kohlrabi, radish, carrot, parsnip, melon, and squash would be missing. For just as there are sexes in the animal kingdom, sexes also exist among plants. In flowering plants the powdery yellow pollen is the male element, and the ovary contains the female element. Sometimes these two elements occur within the same flower, sometimes in different flowers or even in different plants. Pollination—the contact of the pollen with the tip of the ovary (which is generally a sticky knob)—is the important prelude to the fertilization which results in the development of fruits and seeds.

The many insects which seek the nectar, pollen, and foliage of plants for food serve as a practical medium of pollination. This is especially true of the flying insects because they travel from place to place, whereas plants are fixed in position. Insects are ideally suited for this important role. As an individual insect sucks the nectar of a male flower (or of any flower in which the pollen is ripe), pollen grains will adhere to its body. These may be subsequently brushed off within another flower as the insect seeks its food there. As long as the insect goes from flower to flower, collecting and depositing the yellow dust, a continuous process of pollination takes place. Hence, it can be said that the achievement of pollination by insects is only one small part of a complex food cycle which perpetuates species not only of plants but also of the associated insects. A geologic study of the earth's flora and fauna shows a notable rise and development of flowering plants coinciding with the rise and development of the insect fauna.

According to the type of development an insect species undergoes, the larvae may be called maggots, grubs, or caterpillars (complete metamorphosis); or nymphs—when the young bear a resemblance to the adult (incomplete metamorphosis); or naiads—in the case of some aquatic insects characterized by incomplete metamorphosis.

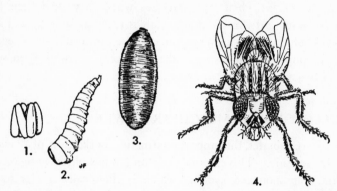

FIGURE 2. **The Four Stages in the Life Cycle of the Common Housefly**
1. Cluster of 5 eggs which will hatch into maggots within 24 hours. (A female lays eggs singly but in batches of from 100 to 150 and may repeat this several times during her lifetime.)
2. A maggot which has hatched from one of these eggs.
3. The pupa from which the adult will emerge in approximately 6 days.
4. The adult which has developed from one of the eggs laid 10 to 14 days previously—under normal summer conditions. (Temperatures below 68° Fahrenheit will retard development.)

When insects going through complete metamorphosis reach the end of their larval development, they prepare themselves for extensive body changes. The larval stage gives way to the pupal or resting stage. For protection during this critical time they construct pupal coverings. The covering itself gives no indication of what is taking place inside because the resting is an outward appearance. In reality there is intense activity within—the development of wings, legs, and other appendages is rapidly taking place. During this period the developing insect is helpless and incapable of feeding. When growth is completed, the outer covering splits and the mature insect draws itself out. Soon after the insect emerges, its body-parts and wings, which are soft, harden and often change color upon contact with the air. Once an insect emerges from its pupal stage it is an adult and it ceases to grow. For instance, a very small winged fly remains a very small winged fly as long as it lives, and big flies do not develop from little flies—as so many people say.

Insects going through incomplete metamorphosis generally omit the pupal stage. Their growth ceases when they shed their final nymphal skin. At this point the adult is ready to lay eggs and start the cycle of the species over again. The entire cycle—from egg to larva, to pupa, to adult—may take from only a few days in some species to seventeen years in others.

SKELETON AND MUSCULAR POWER

Unlike vertebrates, the supporting structure, or skeleton, of all insects is on the outside. This external skeleton is a flexible covering termed "chitin," (pronounced kye-tin) which is chemically similar to the covering of crabs and lobsters. The muscles are completely protected by and attached to the inside surfaces of this chitinous covering.

Much has been written regarding the extraordinary muscular power of insects in comparison to the muscular power of larger animals, but this ratio is often greatly exaggerated by popular writers. According to some investigators, the average insect can pull over twenty times its own weight, and a small leaf-eating beetle (*Donacia*) can pull 42.7 times its own weight. In contrast to these figures, a man can pull but .86, and a horse from .5 to .83, of his own dead weight.

Some of the reasons why insects are more powerful than larger animals are: A chitinous skeleton is lighter than one of bone, thus permitting muscular attachment where it is most advantageous and where it will have superior leverage, unit per unit. Insects have a greater number of muscles. Comparative studies show that in man there are some 792 distinct muscles, whereas in grasshoppers 900 have been described, and in caterpillars about 4,000 have been located. The exceedingly complex muscular system and the cellular makeup of insects are so different from each other and from those of man that a greater variability of muscular movement results.

CLASSIFICATION PRIMER

The insects mentioned in the following pages are grouped under their respective "orders" because an order is the major classification through which the layman can best become acquainted with insects. For the reader's convenience, there follows a very brief explanation of the principles of classifying all natural objects and, in particular, the insects.

All animals, plants, and minerals are classified according to their characteristics and relationships. This system had its origin among the Greek philosophers, especially Aristotle, and explains why many present-day scientific names are of Greek origin. Following the Greeks, the work was continued by the Romans, who not only gave many of the Greek terms a Latin form, but also added many more purely Latin words to keep pace with the accumulation of knowledge. In 1758, the Swedish naturalist Carl von Linné put into general practice the binomial system of nomenclature now adopted by zoologists all over the world. "Taxonomy," therefore, is a man-made artificial system which attempts to organize and catalogue natural objects in one language all over the world, otherwise common names would have little or no meaning outside of a particular locality. This one language is Latin. Von Linné wrote in Latin because in his time that was the usual language of communication among learned men. He even latinized his own name so that he has become known as Carolus Linnaeus, and his system of classification as the Linnaean system.

According to this system, insects belong to the animal kingdom, one of the three great divisions of natural objects. The other two divisions are the plant kingdom and the mineral kingdom.

Kingdoms are divided into PHYLA (singular—Phylum) which are main divisions or branches of a Kingdom.

Phyla are divided into CLASSES, which are groups of individuals ranked together because they possess common characteristics.

Classes are further divided into ORDERS, or finer classifications of one or more groups having certain characteristics in common.

Orders are divided into similarly related groups or FAMILIES, and

Families are divided into GENERA or much more closely related groups.

Genera are broken down into SPECIES or individuals that are essentially alike and that differ from each other only in minor details.

In this system of classification the first three divisions will always be the same for all insects:

KINGDOM—Animal.
PHYLUM—Arthropoda.
CLASS—Insecta.

From this point on, the division into which each insect fits will vary with the characteristics of the insect involved. A few examples of common insects and their classification (as far as species) follows:

Common names:	House fly	Cockroach	Clothes moth
KINGDOM	Animal	Animal	Animal
PHYLUM	Arthropoda	Arthropoda	Arthropoda
CLASS	Insecta	Insecta	Insecta
ORDER	Diptera	Orthoptera	Lepidoptera
FAMILY	Muscidae	Blattidae	Tineidae
GENUS	*Musca*	*Blatta*	*Tinea*
SPECIES	*domestica*	*orientalis*	*pellionella*
Scientific names:	*Musca domestica*	*Blatta orientalis*	*Tinea pellionella*

According to the rules of classification, each organism usually receives two scientific names.   The first name indicates the genus and is always printed with an initial capital. The second name, designating the species, is printed entirely in small letters, except when it is formed from a personal name.   Almost invariably, both generic and specific names are underlined in handwriting and in typescript, and italicized in printed matter.   The sole purpose of this underlining or italicizing is to make scientific names stand out.

Chapter II

Velvet Wings

The Moths and the Butterflies

MOTHS AND BUTTERFLIES IN GENERAL

Moths and butterflies are the insects to which budding entomologists are first attracted—undoubtedly because of their beautiful coloration and interesting patterns. Most people know that the wings of moths and butterflies are covered with a powdery substance which easily rubs off when the wings are handled, but few realize that these powdery particles are in reality minute scales. This is the distinguishing characteristic which suggested Lepidoptera as the name for the Order: *Lepido* = scale; *ptera* = wings. These scales cover the bodies as well as the wings, and follow very definite patterns which can be seen under a high-powered microscope. The patterns may be likened to the overlapping arrangement of shingles on houses, and as the shingles serve to protect the inner surfaces of houses, so do the scales normally serve to protect the wings and bodies of moths and butterflies. These scales vary in shape, size and color, and form the color patterns. If they are rubbed off, the insect is denuded of any protective coloring that it

11

might have had. If *some* of them are rubbed off, from one of the wings especially, the insect's ability to fly is hampered, not only by displacement of weight, but by uneven air flow over the wing's surface. When this happens, the moth or butterfly becomes an easy prey for birds, ants, beetles, and other animals that feed upon insects. Once the scales are lost they are never replaced by a new growth.

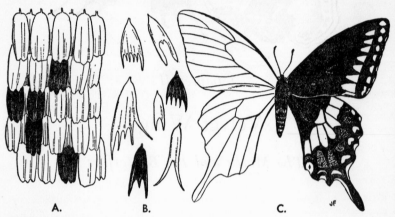

A.   B.   C.

FIGURE 3. Butterfly Scales The over-all color pattern that the human eye sees on moths and butterflies is due to the effect of light—either by absorption or reflection—and may be roughly classified as pigmental as in the case of red, yellow, and blue which fade after the death of the insects, and structural as in the case of iridescent blue, green and violet which are permanent and do not fade upon death.

A. One type of scale arrangement as it would normally appear (under high magnification) on the wing of a butterfly.The five black scales are part of the darker color pattern of the insect.

B. Scales (also highly magnified) of *Papilio*, one of the swallow tail butterflies (illustrated in C) showing how they vary in form on different parts of the body.

C. The right side of the butterfly with the scales in place shows the color pattern. The left side, denuded of scales, shows underlying venation and lack of normal coloration.

Since moths and butterflies are grouped in the same order, the following explanation will help an uninitiated person to tell which is which.

Most moths fly at night, and are attracted to light. They *usually* have feathered antennae, although some species have antennae that are thread-like, while others have antennae that are hooked at the tip. Moths hold their wings flat or fold them against the body when at rest. In the pupal stage they are well-protected by a self-spun cocoon.

Butterflies usually fly by day and can be determined, even from a distance, by the erect manner in which they hold their wings when at rest. They have club-shaped antennae, knobbed at the extreme end. In the pupal stage they are swathed in a thin outer covering, known

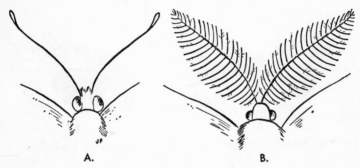

A.   B.

FIGURE 4.   Butterfly and Moth Antennae   The antennae possessed by butterflies usually are knobbed at the extreme ends as in A, and the antennae of moths usually are feathered as in B.

as a chrysalis, in such a way that the various parts of the body are easily discernible. If this chrysalis is handled and gently prodded, one can actually feel the developing insect move.

The larvae of both moths and butterflies are commonly called "caterpillars." They vary in form and appearance but are usually cylindrical, and provided with three pairs of true legs (anteriorly) and two to five pairs of thick, fleshy, jointless tubercles, known as pro-legs (posteriorly).

Moths and butterflies do all their damage while in this caterpillar or larval stage, for it is only then that they are possessed of chewing mouthparts. It is during this early stage, when they do nothing but eat, that they destroy stored woolens, granary products, and crops of the field and forest. These chewing mouthparts are replaced by a "tongue" when the insect reaches maturity—that is, when it becomes a moth or a butterfly. When sucking nectar from blossoms, this "tongue" is extended like a lance. When not in use it is coiled up like a watch spring and lies externally underneath the head. *All* butterflies and a *few* species of moths go through this development. Certain moths do not feed at all when they reach maturity because they lack functional mouthparts, but the life span of such moths is comparatively short—sometimes a matter of a few hours—because then nature's only demand is that they mate and lay eggs for a future generation. As soon as this function has been completed they die.

A.   B.

FIGURE 5. **Butterfly "Tongue"** A. Anterior portion of the head of a butterfly showing the "tongue" as it is extended when sucking nectar from blossoms.

B. Showing position of the "tongue" as it is coiled up externally underneath the head when not in use.

The coloration of moths and butterflies is the source of an Indian legend which explains the creation of these insects and how they were given their beautiful colors. Just as we speak of God, the Indians speak of the Great Spirit, and they believe the Great Spirit was responsible for the creation of the world in which we live. According to this myth, which has been handed down from generation to generation, the Great Spirit created the mountains, the streams, the valleys, and the plains, so that there would be a suitable place for the people to live when he created them later. More than anything else he desired that his people should love nature and seek out its beauties. As an incentive, he made piles and piles of marvellously colored pebbles. There were reds, blues, greens, yellows and purples—in fact, all the colors of the rainbow were in these pebbles. He planned to place them in the beds of all the streams so that his people would be coaxed to investigate the beauties of nature. But suddenly he thought it would be a great pity to hide them away. Then he had an inspiration.

He called in South Wind and commanded him to breathe life into them and bear them away to his summer home. And as South Wind breathed life into them, they slowly rose and flew away—on beautiful wings which had all the colors of the rainbow. According to Indian legend, these pebbles were the first moths and butterflies.

On prehistoric Hopi pottery, moths and butterflies are among the most prominently figured insects. These symbols constantly appear on secular and ceremonial paraphernalia. The famous Butterfly Dance or "Bulitikibi" is said to have been introduced by the prominent and powerful Butterfly Clan of one of the Hopi pueblos. It is a ceremonial dance performed by youths and maidens in the open plaza of their village where the onlookers can view it from their housetops. The leaders of this clan plan the changing figures and drill the dancers for several days preceding the performance. The dance begins at noon and ends at sundown, with intermissions for rest and changes of costume. The maidens carry little sprigs in their hands and wear wooden tablets on their heads—a symbol of clouds. They dance with downcast eyes, scarcely moving their feet. The youths shake rattles and lift their knees high in the air with each step they take. All the dancers move silently. Another group, comprising the chorus, sings the dance music while beating a steady rhythm on drums. The entire ceremonial is a supplication for good crops, and the accompanying words are as follows:

Poli Tuwa Tawi	*Butterfly Dance Song*
Humuicita cingölawu	Now for the corn blossoms we wrestle
Mozhicita congölawu	Now for the bean blossoms we wrestle
Itam totim nikiang	We are youths mid the corn
Uyi stonaka ngöti-tiwani	Chasing each other in sport
Tu veval manatu amuni	Playing with butterfly maidens
Peyo peyo!	Hither, hither!
Umumu tani	Thunder will hither move
Ita ayatoni	We shall summon the thunder hither
Uyi manatu	That the maiden plants
Omi nawungwinani	Upwards may help one another to grow

CATERPILLARS OF MOTHS

Caterpillars—the larvae of Lepidoptera—are frequently ornamented with hornlike protuberances, are more or less covered with hair, and vary greatly in color and size. A few species are covered with hairs which are true poison spines and serve as an effective means of defense. These spines are also capable of inflicting serious skin rashes upon anyone handling them carelessly, and internal irritation may take place when poison-spined caterpillars are extremely numerous. For example, from time to time the saddleback caterpillar (*Sibine stimulea*) occurs in great numbers in New England. Their small hair-like spines are easily broken off, picked up by the wind and thus transported for many miles. When this spine-laden air is breathed into the lungs the spines cause great bronchial irritation. In the past such occurrences have attained minor epidemic proportions in certain localities.

FIGURE 6. The Saddleback A pretty-looking caterpillar, over-all pale green in color with a brown saddle with white areas, that one is tempted to pick up to admire. This should be avoided, however, because this species of caterpillar has sharp, brittle spines which are connected with poison glands. If handled it may cause skin irritation much like that caused by brushing against nettling or stinging plants.

When the brown-tail moth is in the caterpillar stage it has poisonous hairs which are barbed. These hairs, when freed by molting, are often carried by the wind and, upon coming in contact with the skin of the face, neck, hands, or other exposed parts of the body, give rise to "Brown-Tail Moth rash." This moth (*Euproctis phaeorrhoea*), although originally a native of Europe, arrived in the United States as a stowaway and is now well established here.

Medicine men of various primitive tribes have noted the rash-producing power of the natural "arrows" or "stings" of certain hairy caterpillars and have used them as a basis for some of their witchcraft.

In the Pomeroon District of British Guiana in South America, the medicine men prepare the tribesmen for a hunt in this fashion: Into incisions made on a man's thighs and wrists, they deliberately rub the hairs of those caterpillars which they know have great irritating power. This produces painful rashes and thereby supposedly insures the success of the chase.   Since physical fitness is a fundamental requisite in a primitive tribe, it is probable that such trials play a part in eliminating the physically unfit.   Tribesmen who subject themselves to this painful experience know that fever generally results from the poison thus introduced into their bodies, and that they may even die, yet they willingly undergo this ordeal as a means of proving their virility.

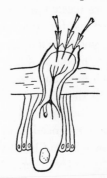

In the region of the head-hunters of the Amazon River in South America there exists a big hairy caterpillar (called "wambángu" by the natives) which is caught and used by sorcerers for bewitching purposes.   The procedure is somewhat as follows: The medicine man mixes a concoction containing these poisonous hairs and places it upon an arrow. Then, with an incantation, the arrow is shot into the air in the general direction of the victim on whom the spell is to be cast.   It is practically impossible to get details of just why and how medicine men do such things— their secrets are handed down to their successors by word of mouth only—but it is generally known that mental suggestion plays an important part in the successful outcome of such spells, for in most cases the victim is somehow apprised of the curse cast upon him.

FIGURE   7.   Poison Gland   of   Brown-Tail Moth An enlarged diagram of one of the poison glands of the caterpillar of the brown-tail moth, showing three barbed hairs.

In the primitive medicine of seventeenth century Europe, an oil made from clothes moths was said to "cure warts, deafness, and leprosy, and when mixed with tar, to be good in all sorts of rebellious ulcers, botches, scabs and whittles."   Another European custom was the medicinal use of canker-worms, the caterpillars which are such great pests of shade trees.   These were collected in great numbers, burned, and the ashes, when put into the nostrils, were said to stop bleeding.   A powder made of these ashes was also prescribed for epilepsy.

Insect larvae are used today for a variety of purposes—as food, as weather forecasters, and as an oddity of commerce. The Bushmen of Africa feed upon the caterpillars of many moths. In the Bugong Mountains of Central Australia some tribesmen not only eat the caterpillars of certain moths but feed upon the adult moths themselves, which they call "bugong." The natives remove the wings and numerous body hairs by stirring the moths on fire-heated ground. After being roasted in this manner the moths may be eaten while still warm or stored for later use. The bodies of these moths abound in oil and are said to be nutlike in flavor. Evidently they are an acquired taste for they produce illness when first eaten, but this reaction lessens with each meal and the natives seem to thrive on them.

In the Cascade and Sierra Mountains of North America, Indian tribesmen seek the large caterpillars of the pandora moths which feed upon the needles of the yellow pines. The full-grown caterpillars measure from two to two and one-half inches in length and are as fat as an index finger. Normally these caterpillars live on the pine trees, far out of reach, but in order to pass into the pupal stage they descend in great numbers to burrow into the soil. Just before this takes place the Indians build fires under the trees and stupefy the caterpillars by the smudge. This causes them to loosen their holds on the trees and fall to the ground where they are collected in baskets. They are then prepared as food by being dried over a bed of hot ashes or by being boiled in water.

In Mexico, today, one may buy a "tidbit" called "*gusanos*" which is the Spanish for "worms." This word is applied indiscriminately to caterpillars, earthworms, and beetle grubs which are found in the hearts of the agave plants. They are eaten after having been crisply fried. Most people consider this as a repugnant custom of savages, but in the United States people are eating fried caterpillars with relish. Close to the Mexican border, "*gusanos*" are served as thirst-producers at cocktail parties. In recent years Mexico has been canning and exporting "*gusanos*" and they may now be purchased in the better delicatessen and department stores of our larger cities. They are advertised as "delicious delicacies, especially with cocktails."

In China and Burma, after the silk has been removed from the cocoons of the silkworms, the pupae are eaten. This is possible because as part of the process of reeling the cocoons must first be dropped into very hot water, which actually is sufficient to cook the pupa within the cocoon.   Thus the girls who unreel the silk have a plentiful supply of freshly cooked food before them, which they eat intermittently during the long hours of their working day.   In Burma these pupae are known as Po-gaung-gyaw and are sold for about 1½ rupees (about 75¢) per viss (3½ lbs.).   If fried in fat and salted they are eaten immediately, but if boiled they may be stored for future consumption. Such pupae are considered a treat and frequently are presented as gifts.

In this country during the past few years the "woolly bears" have been stealing the headlines as weather forecasters.   "Woolly bears" are caterpillars of moths and there are over 2,000 species of them.   They are black at both ends, with a reddish-brown mid-band which may vary in width from year to year.   They are about 1¼ inches long, characterized by being very hairy, or woolly-looking.   They were mentioned as early as 1608 by Edward Topsell, a naturalist, who said they were called "Palmer" worms—so named after the "palmer" or wandering monk—because of their roving habits, roughness of appearance, and ruggedness (they are observed late in the season).   He also mentioned that they were known as "beare worms." In modern phraseology all of these terms could conceivably be the equivalent of "woolly bears."

It has been a folk belief of long standing that local winter weather may be predicted by observing the width of the reddish-brown band on these caterpillars.   The common species chosen for this prognosis is the Tiger moth, *Isia isabella*.   This belief is now being seriously investigated by Dr. C. Howard Curran of The American Museum of Natural History.   After four years' observations (1947–1951), and using this band-width as a basis, he made weather predictions which, surprisingly, were more accurate than some meteorological forecasts.   The prediction for 1952 was for a more severe winter than the four previous ones, but this did not prove so.   However, Dr. Curran stresses the fact that in order to make forecasts with any degree of scientific accuracy it will take at least fifteen years of measuring or counting the segments comprising the reddish-brown band and correlating his data.   The theory is that the narrower the reddish-brown band, the colder and longer will be the winter; the wider the band the milder the winter.

The width of the band supposedly forecasts, in terms of degrees Fahrenheit, the "average" temperature for the entire winter, and has nothing to do with a cold spell of short duration, or with an occasional storm such as the blizzard of 1888, which happened during a year when the mid-band on the woolly bear was wider than usual and a mild winter was predicted.   However, in spite of the occurrence of the greatest blizzard on record, the "average" for that winter was mild.

At the approach of very cold weather the "woolly bears" hibernate, being one of the few species of caterpillars known to do so, and with the coming of spring emerge from their hibernation and immediately look for food.   They feed for a short time and then pupate in a cocoon made up of hairs from their own cast larval skins mixed with silk which they secrete from glands within their own bodies.   As soon as development is completed they emerge from their cocoons as adult moths. Normally there are two broods per year.

That curiosity—the Mexican jumping bean—is really a one-room apartment for the tiny caterpillar of the small bean moth that is known to entomologists as *Carpocapsa saltitans*.   This moth lays its eggs in the bean flower, or in the still green and tender bean seed pod.   By the time the egg hatches into a caterpillar it is inside the hardened shell, enclosed by the juicy meat of the bean.   The tiny caterpillar slowly feeds upon the interior of the bean until only a hollow shell remains, and then lines the chamber with silk and transforms into a pupa.   As the pupa twists and turns within, the bean moves or "jumps."   During this pupal stage, which lasts for several weeks, the bean becomes a "jumping bean" and as such is marketable.   Millions of them are sold each year.   As the pupa reaches the end of its transformation it works its way through the bean capsule.   When it reaches the outside world, it draws itself out of its pupal covering, unfolds its wings, and is on its way—seeking a young bean pod on which to lay eggs and thus perpetuate the jumping species.

SILKWORMS

The silkworm moth, *Bombyx mori*, is variously called the Japanese, the Chinese, or the Mulberry Silkworm.   Traditionally the home of this moth is China, but the fact that its eggs hatch only if *first* exposed to natural or artificial cold lends weight to the theory that the insects' original home was in the high altitudes—probably the central parts of Asia whence the Chinese may have carried it in prehistoric times. Actually there are many kinds of silkworms in addition to *Bombyx mori*, each of which produces silk of a different kind and each of which needs special food and care. Some of the better known producers of usable silk are the Syrian Silkworm, the Eri Silkworm (of India), the Japanese Oak Silkworm, the Oriental Luna, and the Ailanthus Silkworm.

Bombyx mori has been cultivated for so long a time that it can no longer exist without being cared for by humans. It is a true domestic insect. Its domestication has resulted in this moth's loss of power of flight, and as a result of artificial selection the silk glands have become very large—each of the two glands being nearly five times as long as the body. Controlled breeding has also resulted in increasing the quantity and quality of silk. The silk produced by the caterpillars of undomesticated (wild) moths is considerably less in quantity and much coarser in texture.

Silk is the product of the cocoon of the silkworm and some twenty-five hundred of these peanut-sized cocoons are required to make a single pound of silk. For centuries fabrics made of silk were considered a luxury which only the nobility or the very rich could afford. Beyond the borders of China this fashion seems to have been established about 81 B.C., when Pompey, returning from his Asiatic campaign, wore a silk robe which he had obtained in Persia, where a few silk garments had been brought from China by way of camel caravan.

The story of how silk was accidentally discovered has many variations, but the most accepted version maintains that about 4,000 years ago the Chinese Empress, Si-Ling, was curiously inspecting a cocoon from her garden when it slipped from her fingers and dropped into her hot cup of tea. As she handled the retrieved cocoon, she noticed that from the softened exterior it was possible to unwind a strong and lustrous fiber in one long thread. She experimented in weaving some of this thread and the result was so startling that she soon had many helpers to seek methods of rearing the silkworm caterpillars and of winding off the silk to be spun into cloth. Thus began China's main industry, which was to last for many centuries—the production of raw silk and the manufacture of silk fabrics. To this day, silk is called "Si" in China, in honor of the clever Chinese Empress Si-Ling. She was placed among the Chinese deities as the "Goddess of the Silkworms" and every spring, when the mulberry leaves appear, the Chinese hold a feast in her honor.

For centuries it fell upon the women of China to raise the insects at home and to unwind the raw silk from the cocoons. It required an infinite amount of patience and a great amount of hand labor. Members of a family often incubated the eggs by carrying them inside their clothing in specially prepared egg-cards. These egg-cards kept the eggs separated and prevented crushing. Each female moth lays between 200 and 350 eggs which hatch in a week to ten days. When the eggs hatched into caterpillars it meant twenty-four-hours-a-day-care in feeding the caterpillars on fresh mulberry leaves, keeping them at the proper temperature and moisture, guarding against the numerous diseases which attack the silkworms, and removing their debris. The caterpillars pass through four molts, or changes of skin, and reach maturity in about six to seven weeks. During this time their appetites are voracious; it is estimated that one ounce of eggs produce silkworms that devour approximately fifteen hundred pounds of leaves.

In order to develop the industry some Chinese rulers ordered every man to plant a few mulberry trees on his land; others gave each man 50 acres of land on condition that he plant 20 acres of it with mulberry. It was forbidden, under penalty of severe punishment, to export silkworms or silkworm eggs from China, or to furnish information on methods of rearing silkworms or manufacturing silk. The many restrictions which China imposed on the silk industry succeeded in keeping the art a mystery from Europeans for hundreds of years, until about 550 A.D., two Justinian monks succeeded in smuggling the eggs of silkworms into Constantinople where the European branch of the industry started.

The silkworm, before changing into a pupa, spins a thread three deniers thick which thins out to two deniers toward the end. The threads are spun by the caterpillar in a succession of S-shaped loops totaling a length of approximately 4,000 yards of silk on each cocoon of which only from 300 to 1,000 yards are commercially usable. Hence, the woman reeling the silk from the cocoons must exercise skill in selection and unwinding so that a uniform thickness is maintained throughout. They accomplish this by adding more thread from other cocoons. The silkworms' own spinning is much too fine to be worked, so that from four to twenty threads—six to eight as a rule—are led together prior to being brought to reel, since the silk must be of a standardized thickness before it is commercially acceptable.

Silkworms have many uses beyond their value as a source of fabrics. The same glands that produce silk are also a source of surgical stitching material and fishing-line leaders. In preparation the silkworm is opened, the silk sacs are removed, and their gummy contents (from which the worm spins its silk) are taken out and stretched into thin threads, twelve to fourteen inches in length and having a tensile strength of three to five pounds per thread. Silk gut is still used for surgical stitching, but for fishing-line leaders it has been largely replaced by nylon. Leaders made of nylon are more easily manufactured because they can be turned out in varying lengths and strengths—far in excess of the restrictions inherent in silkworm glands.

In middle and northern California there are wild giant silkworm moths (*Samia euryalus* and *Telea polyphemus*) that spin cocoons about five inches long. These cocoons are so tough that the Indians of the region split them open, remove the bodies, insert a few pebbles in each cocoon, bind them singly or in groups, and tie them to the ends of sticks to make rattles and musical instruments for their ritualistic ceremonies.

The silkworm has also played a part in adding to our knowledge of medicine. The proof that disease was due to germs was not forthcoming until Louis Pasteur (in 1865) responded to an urgent call from the French Government for help in solving the famous "silkworm disease" epidemic. At that time many people in southern France depended upon the cultivation of silkworms for a livelihood, and the industry was threatened with ruin because the silkworms were dying of disease. It took five years of research for Pasteur to discover the origin of the silkworm disease and to show that it is caused by germs that were contagious.   Armed with the knowledge Pasteur gave them, the silkworm growers were then able to control the epidemic, but the silk industry in France never fully regained its former status. Pasteur's proof focused general attention upon the germ theory of disease and thus served as an important stepping stone in the study of contagion.

Silk has been successfully produced in many countries all over the world, including Portugal, Spain, France, Greece, Brazil, and even in the United States, but only in the Orient did the production of raw silk maintain its commercially profitable status.   For the weaving of silk into cloth the leading manufacturing center, about fifty years ago, was Paterson, New Jersey, when Paterson was world-famous as The Silk City of America.   Because of the tremendous amount of labor involved in the production of silk, Occidental industries could not long compete with the cheap labor costs in the Orient.   And while the silk industry had its inception in China and flourished there for centuries, by the beginning of World War II, Japan had become the world's greatest silk-producing country, as well as the greatest exporter of silk products.   At that time the United States was the largest importer and user of silk.   Now, with the discovery of nylon and other synthetic fibers, modern science has dealt the silk industry what may prove to be its death blow, for chemistry has succeeded in creating substances which, in many ways, are superior to the natural silk fiber.

MOTHS

In spite of many common beliefs as to why moths are attracted to light, the specific factors involved in this behavior pattern have not yet been fully determined by scientists.

One superstitious belief dates back to olden times when the moth was called "The Soul," because people fancied that the souls of the dead flew at night seeking light.   A small yellowish moth which flies about the fire at night is called "tûñ tăwû" by the Cherokee Indians— a name implying that it goes in and out of the fire.   When it flits too near and falls into the blaze the Cherokee say "tûñ tăwû is going to bed." Because of its affinity for the fire it is invoked by the Indian doctor in what they call "Fire Diseases," among which sore eyes and frostbite are included.

A poetic explanation of why moths are attracted to light was written by Mrs. A. L. Ruter Dufour on June 24, 1864:

> One summer night, says a legend old,
>   A Moth a Firefly sought to woo:
> "Oh, wed me, I pray, thou bright star-child,
>   To win thee there's nothing I'd dare not do."
>
> "If thou art sincere," the Firefly cried,
>   "Go—bring me a light that will equal my own;
> Not until then will I deign be thy bride;"—
>   Undaunted the Moth heard her mocking tone.
>
> Afar he beheld a brilliant torch,
>   Forward he dashed, on rapid wing,
> Into the light to bear it hence;—
>   When he fell a scorched and blighted thing.—
>
> Still ever the Moths in hope to win,
>   Unheeding the lesson, the gay Firefly,
> Dash, reckless, the dazzling torch within,
>   And, vainly striving, fall and die!

There is one group of moths which has attracted the attention of country folk on both sides of the Atlantic. These are the sphinx moths, also commonly called hawk moths or hummingbird moths. When caterpillars of these moths are disturbed, they rear themselves up in such a manner that there is a fancied resemblance to the Egyptian Sphinx—hence the name. In a tomato patch, look for the common big green tomato worm which belongs to this group. Prod one, and then watch its reaction, and its resemblance to the "Sphinx." In this stage they are usually referred to as sphinx caterpillars, but when they have completed their metamorphosis and emerge as adults they are more often referred to as hawk moths or hummingbird moths. This is not surprising for then they are unusually large and heavy and actually resemble hummingbirds. In some ways they even act like hummingbirds; for instance, in their manner of flying and their habit of hovering about a flower while sipping nectar from it.

On this side of the Atlantic, within the borders of our own country, some people believe a sphinx moth is a *cross* between a hummingbird and a butterfly.   Among the Indians of California the belief is that this moth *turns into* a hummingbird.   Interestingly enough, these moths fly by day or in early evening, contrary to the nocturnal habits of most moths.

Another of these large sphinx moths, confined to Europe, is called "The Death's Head" because the conspicuous markings on their backs resemble a human skull with the thigh bones crossed beneath—somewhat like the emblem employed by pharmacists to denote poisonous contents.   These moths also make a squeaking sound which the superstitious associate with the anguished moaning of a child.   They regard it as an omen of coming evil or a forerunner of death.

BUTTERFLIES

The butterfly seems to have derived its name from the common yellow species (the cabbage butterfly) because it is first seen in the early spring or butter season.   In the earliest form of the language (Anglo-Saxon) they were called "Buttor-fleage" or "buter flege," meaning butter fly.   The present German names, also of long standing, are likewise associated with dairy products: "Schmeterling," from Schmeten = cream; also, "Molkendieb" = the whey thief.

Many kinds of butterflies are known to be extensive natural travelers. The Monarch butterfly, so common in our northern latitudes, flies thousands of miles in order to spend the winter months in the Gulf States.   In the fall of the year these butterflies assemble in countless numbers along our northeastern and northwestern coasts.   They cling to the leaves and branches of trees and bushes which actually bend down under their weight.   At some given signal, not yet known to science, they arise in a cloud and migrate southward.   How they keep their direction over land and over bodies of water in the face of strong winds and even storms is something else not yet known.   However, it has been established that butterflies of the western and the eastern species return northward in great numbers the following spring in order to lay their eggs for a new generation.

In California, the municipality of Pacific Grove has passed stringent laws to protect the Monarch butterflies; to destroy them may bring one a fine of five hundred dollars or possibly a six-month jail sentence. In this little town, sheltered from the broad Pacific, a strange recurring phenomenon of nature takes place. For years, with the same accuracy of timing as the celebrated swallows of Capistrano, a mass migration of millions of Monarch butterflies arrive to settle in Pacific Grove each winter. These fragile creatures travel in a body more than three thousand miles, and always seek the same grove of pine trees that their ancestors sought before them. Starting in isolated parts of Alaska, they fly the most direct route, being joined by more Monarch butterflies in Canada and the northern United States. For the final lap they wing their way over twenty miles of ocean. In mid-winter, when butterflies are seldom seen elsewhere, the streets and lawns of this California town are filled with golden wings. With the coming of spring they leave the little town as mysteriously as they arrive.

Instructions to observe butterflies for determining the points of the compass have in the past been issued to men expecting to travel in the jungles of

FIGURE 8. Monarch butterflies clinging to leaves in process of migration.

South America. The basis in fact is that for many months, in many parts of the tropics, butterflies migrate by the tens of thousands in very definite directions. In northeastern South America this path of migration is from southwest to northeast, so that a man lost in the jungle, without compass or benefit of the sun, can determine his direction by observing the butterflies' direction of flight.

Many butterflies have been captured so that their beautifully-colored wings might be used for decorative purposes. This was especially true of the large Morpho butterflies of South America; their iridescent, brilliantly-colored wings were utilized extensively for making jewelry, trays, and framed miniature silhouettes. The trade became so profitable that such butterflies were caught in large numbers. As a result, the danger of extinction became so imminent that certain South American governments passed laws prohibiting their capture and export.

Quite the rage at the turn of the century was the making of huge framed pictures using pinned insect specimens, with butterflies composing the central design. The American Museum of Natural History had a few of these elaborately-framed, glass-covered pictures, and a particularly impressive one, measuring about three feet square, was in the form of a great lyre, utilizing small iridescent beetles and thousands of vari-colored butterflies for the background. In another such framed picture, beetles outlined a design in the form of a horseshoe which was centered within a six-pointed star. The background was also elaborately filled in with many decorative species of moths and butterflies.

The Blackfoot Indians believe that dreams are brought to us in sleep by the butterfly (*ap-u-nni*). It is therefore customary for a woman of the tribe to embroider the sign of the butterfly in beads or quills on a small piece of buckskin, and this she ties in her baby's hair when she wishes it to go to sleep. At the same time she sings to her child a lullaby in which the butterfly is asked to come flying about and put her baby to sleep. The best explanation of this belief is that if one watches this insect for a length of time, its silent, graceful, rhythmic fluttering will induce sleep.

The butterfly symbol of these Indians is a design with eight points, roughly resembling a Maltese cross. This usually appears just below the smoke vent at the back of their more elaborately ornamented lodges. Whenever this symbol appears on a lodge it signifies that the designs and colors adorning that lodge are not those of the mortal Indian who painted them but were shown to him in a dream by the Great Spirit.

The Zuni Indians of our southwestern states believe that butterflies play a role in the prediction of weather. To them the early appearance of butterflies indicates fair weather. They say: "When the white butterfly comes, comes also the summer;" and "When the white butterfly flies from the southwest, expect rain."

When it comes to superstitious beliefs, butterflies indicate many things to many people, but it is interesting to note that, with butterflies as with other insects, many similar occurrences are interpreted to have contradictory meanings in different localities. For instance, in Louisiana it is believed that good luck will follow soon after a white butterfly comes into your house and flies around you, but in Maryland the belief is that it supposedly foretells death. Any butterfly flying in one's face is a sign of immediate cold weather to some; others specify that a *yellow* butterfly flying in one's face indicates sufficient frost within ten days to turn the leaves the color of the butterfly. And in western Pennsylvania, when the chrysalids are found suspended from the underside of rails and heavy branches, as if to seek a covering from rain, then extremely wet weather is predicted; if they are found on slender branches, then a spell of fair weather is predicted.

Many lovers of nature may be interested to learn that gardens can be planted that will attract butterflies, bees, and many beneficial insects that destroy harmful ones, simply by cultivating a succession of flowering plants to which these insects are attracted. Among these would be crocuses, snowdrops, michaelmas daisies, hyacinths, cornflowers, columbine, sweet-scented mignonette, forsythia, rhododendrons, rose of sharon, and especially the so-called butterfly bush—the buddleias. Beebalm (monarda) primarily attracts bees, but it also attracts butterflies, hummingbird moths, and hummingbirds. If some of these plants predominate, one will enjoy a procession of brightly-colored wings.

Information of the kind contained in this book is scattered through thousands of miscellaneous publications. Much of it consists of mere listings of brief proverbs and beliefs; some extremely localized and some widely known. If nothing can be added in clarification, many will be listed, as found, under a miscellaneous heading at the end of each order, such as the one which follows.

MISCELLANEOUS

PROVERBS:

"Patience and the mulberry leaf become a silk gown."
"The butterfly that brushes against thorns will tear its wings."
"The moth does the most mischief to the finest garments."
"A worm is in the bud of youth and at the root of old age."
"The silkworm-moth eyebrow of a woman is the ax that cuts down the wisdom of man." (Chinese proverb.) [The antennae of the newly-emerged moth are very short and feathery and arched back over the two eyes so as to give the appearance of a beautiful pair of eyebrows.]

GENERAL:

If a measuring worm (caterpillar) measures your whole length you will die. (In some sections of the country the same saying substitutes "girth" for "length.")
If a moth lights on the mother of a newly born infant the death of the latter is sure to follow.
A butterfly in the house is a wedding sign.
It causes bad luck to pull off butterfly wings.
Seeing caterpillars late in the fall predicts a mild winter.
Kill the first butterfly you see each year, or you will have bad luck all through the year.—Devonshire.
Night-flying white moths are souls of the departed.—Yorkshire.
Butterflies are souls of the dead waiting to pass through Purgatory.—Ireland. [The ancient Egyptians had a somewhat similar belief—that the soul left the dead as a butterfly emerges from a chrysalis].

SYMBOL:

Lebanon displayed a mulberry leaf, cocoon, moth and silkworm, all on one stamp, in honor of the convention of silk producers held there in 1930.

Chapter III

Insects in Armor

The Beetles

Beetles, which are four-winged insects, are distinguished from all other insects because they have a front pair of thick, rigid wings that form hard shields. These serve to cover and protect the more delicate hind pair of wings used for flying. The front wings, technically known as elytra, suggested the scientific name of Coleoptera for the Order: *Coleo* = sheath; *ptera* = wings. When not in use, the hind wings are folded underneath the front pair. The Cherokee Indians were so impressed by the "armor-plating" of these insects that they called beetles "insects with shells," a name interestingly similar to the translation "sheath-wings" from the original Greek—and perhaps even more apt.

There are approximately 250,000 described species of beetles and they form the largest single order in the entire animal kingdom. They are the greatest "armor-clad" group of insects and their habits are extremely varied: They live in soil, in water, and in vegetable or animal

31

matter, feed upon practically everything, and are important as scavengers. They are also used in medicine, and as food.

The larvae of bettles, commonly called grubs, are highly nutritious. Malabar coolies, and also many natives of South America and Africa, roast and eat the larvae normally found living in their areas. The Greeks and the Romans realized the nutritional value of grubs, for it is recorded that at the time of their greatest periods of luxurious living they included the *Coccus* grub on their menus. This is the grub of a large beetle living in the stems of trees, particularly oaks.

Of the grubs used for food in many parts of the world, the grub of the palm weevil, a beetle with an elongated snout, seems to be the one preferred. These fatty grubs, which are found in the tops of certain palm trees, are eaten by the Jivaro-Canelos Indians of Peru and by the Creoles in the Island of Barbados. The Creoles consider them a rare dish indeed. They say that when roasted the taste is like that of the marrow of beef bones.

The Spaniards in Santiago of Tucuman, when traveling on expedition in search of wild honey, which they find in the hollows of trees in the forests, make it a practice to cleave certain palm trees on their way. On their return they examine the purposely damaged tree parts, knowing that in the meantime grubs will have been attracted to the injuries. They usually find large ones, which they fry and relish as a delicious food.

The aborigines in Australia, usually sorely pressed for food, consider grubs such an essential item of nourishment that they eat them raw, immediately upon finding them. The natives definitely know that these grubs are good for them, but they do not know why; it so happens that this is their only source of protein. These aborigines are noted for having developed an abnormally acute sense of hearing, no doubt as a result of their unique method of detecting the whereabouts of grubs. They tap fallen trees and logs and by the sound are able to determine whether they contain any grubs. The natives will not proceed to pry open these trees and logs—a laborious and time-consuming task—until their supersensitive ears record the *proper* reverberation. Obviously, the necessity of saving time and strength is a vital matter to a hungry people who spend most of their time searching for food.

In the freshwater ponds of China a great industry is centered around the breeding and raising of water beetles. These diving beetles (of the family Dytiscidae) are a great delicacy to the Chinese, and a special tidbit to their children. Chinese children will munch away on these dried insects for hours with as much relish as American children munching pieces of candy.

FIGURE 9.

According to a Cherokee Indian myth, a beetle of this same family played an important part in the creation of the world. In the beginning all was water. Dâyuní si (Beaver's grandchild) dove to the bottom to see what he could learn. When he touched bottom he scooped up some soft mud in his claws and brought it to the surface. As soon as this mud reached the surface it spread and grew on every side. And so it is that to Dâyuní si the Cherokees give the credit of bringing up the first earth in the creation of the world. They believe that the earth is a great island floating in a sea of water and is suspended at each of the four cardinal points by a cord hanging down from the sky vault of solid rock. When the earth grows old and worn out the cords will break and cause the earth to sink into the ocean, whereupon all will be water again.

In the beginning, after the world was created, the birds, beasts, fishes, insects, and plants all had the power to talk. They had chiefs, councils, and town houses. They mingled with human beings upon terms of equality, and all spoke the same language. By comparison, the animals we know today are poor in intellect and small in size, and are not descendants of these mythical, perfect types. At first the people and all the animals lived in harmony, but the people increased so rapidly that soon the mammals and the insects found themselves cramped for room. To add to their miseries, man began to slaughter the larger animals for food and skins, while the smaller animals, such as the insects, were trodden upon. In vengeful self-defense the insects met in council. Chief of the council was Grubworm (*Cotinis nitida*); related to the sacred scarab beetle of Egypt. At this council, one suggestion so amused Grubworm that he shouted with glee and in his excitement fell over backwards. When he tried to get on his feet he could not do so and had to wriggle off on his head—and Grubworm has had to wriggle ever since.

It was at this council that each insect devised a new disease wherewith to plague man. That, relates this myth, is why and how we come to suffer from insect-transmitted diseases. The Cherokee's generic name for all sorts of small insects and worms is tsgâya, and according to the Cherokee doctors these tsgâya are responsible for nearly every human ailment. Their belief that disease organisms are transmitted from animals to man existed hundreds of years before this fact was confirmed by scientific research.

Our Cochiti Indians from the Southwest associate a genus of beetles called *Eleodes* with another creation myth. They relate that long, long ago, this beetle was assigned to place the stars in the sky. Filled with ego because of the important part entrusted to him, he grew more and more casual as the days went by, until one day he carelessly dropped the stars and they scattered all over the sky, forming what we call the Milky Way. So ashamed was he at what he had done, because of his carelessness, that even to this day he will hide his face in the dirt when anyone approaches him.

Eleodes is interestingly set apart from most other beetles in that it cannot fly; hence it is confined to a terrestrial life. As one approaches it, it will lower its head to the ground, raise its hind quarters and emit a disagreeable odor, somewhat in the same manner as does the skunk. This is a means of defense, and an effective one against its enemies.

In the prehistoric ruins of New Mexico and Arizona, strange black and red beetles (the Rhipiphoridae) wander among the scattered heaps of broken pottery. The Navajos look upon this beetle with a strange mixture of awe and amusement and call him "Asanay-ehe"—the pot carrier. They say he comes by his name quite honestly, for "does he not carry two tiny pots upon his shoulders?" The "pots"

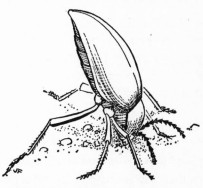

FIGURE 10. Eleodes The beetle of the Cochiti Indian legend showing the manner in which it buries its head.

which this beetle is said to carry upon "his shoulders" are in reality vestigial wing covers, but they actually do look like tiny jars. They also say that this insect is in league with a monster that breaks the pottery of the dead and that it is this beetle which smashes into small fragments the pottery which is found at ancient village sites. According to the Navajos, this myth explains why pottery that dates back to a long dead civilization is almost always found broken.

As we shall see in the following pages, beetles have contributed to a notable list of real and fancied remedies. The jaws (mandibles) of the stag beetle, for example, were worn by an afflicted person under the name of "horns of scarabaei" in the case of convulsions, and an oil prepared by soaking the beetle itself was said to cure earache. Presumably this was the same beetle that was recommended by Thomas Moffett, a seventeenth century writer of natural history, to be worn as an amulet for "an ague of pains, and contraction of the tendons if applied to the affected parts, and if tied to the necks of children it enables them to retain their urine." An image of this same beetle, engraved upon an emerald, was claimed to be protection against all witchcraft and to keep away "the headache, which truly is no small mischief, especially to great drinkers."

SPANISH FLY

"Cantharides," "blister beetles," and "Spanish fly," are names applied interchangeably to beetles used principally for medicinal purposes because of their blistering qualities. Although they have been known for generations as "Spanish fly," they are neither Spanish in origin nor are they flies.

The blister beetles differ from other beetles in that one part of their life span is spent destroying the pests of man and the other in destroying the crops of man. For instance, the common blister beetles found in America feed, in their early stages, upon grasshopper eggs and in that way are helpful in cutting down the number of grasshoppers that might otherwise emerge. At this stage they are called "triungulins" and are very active, running around freely from one burrow to another and feeding voraciously upon any grasshopper eggs they find. However, when they complete their development and emerge as adults they frequently are great destroyers of potatoes and other cultivated crops.

The common gray and black blister beetles we have in this country are sometimes called "old-fashioned potato beetles." These American beetles have blistering qualities, but are not the commercial source of "cantharidin"—the term which, for centuries, has designated the active blistering substance contained in the bodies of blister beetles. The word "cantharidin" has been loosely used; it may apply either to the dry powdered beetles themselves, or to the preserved fluid extract from their bodies. Commercial cantharidin is obtained from blister beetles in Spain, south Russia, Hungary, Sicily, Poland, Rumania, and southern Europe, for thus far its artificial manufacture has been unsuccessful.

When alive these blister beetles, or Spanish flies, have a strong, penetrating, fetid odor, comparable to that of mice, and it is by this odor that swarms of them may be detected at considerable distances.

The adults feed upon the leaves of trees and shrubs such as the white poplar, ash, elder, privet, and lilac.

Life history studies of these beetles in Spain, Italy, and southern France show that the eggs are laid by the females during the latter part of June. They are laid in small cylindrical holes in the ground and about a week elapses before they hatch into larvae that measure approximately one millimeter in length. Immediately upon hatching, the larvae crawl up the stems of flowers. They then attach themselves to bees or wasps and are thus transported to the bees' hive or the wasps' nest. Once in the colony they loosen their hold and for several months the blister beetle larvae feed upon the honey and beebread stored up for the use of the occupants. When ready to pupate, just prior to becoming adults, they drop to the ground for the last stage of their development. Then in May or June of the following year, when mature, they emerge from the ground in swarms. It is at this time that they are collected in great quantities.

The time preferred for collecting blister beetles is in the morning, soon after sunrise, because then they are torpid from the cold night and easily loosen their hold when the trees and shrubs are shaken or their branches beaten with poles. The insects fall upon linen cloths which have been spread underneath the trees. The people who collect these beetles cover their hands with gloves and protect their faces with masks because of the irritation and blistering that would result if the insects came in contact with the surface of their skin.

To kill and preserve the blister beetles as quickly as possible, before they exude any of their valuable secretion, the beetles are plunged into vinegar diluted with water, or else placed in sieves and exposed to the fumes of vinegar, ammonia, chloroform, burning sulphur, or carbon bisulphide. The current method of killing the beetles by the steam of vinegar is practically the same as the technique used in ancient times. They are next dried naturally in the sun, or in specially built ovens. When dried the beetles are stored in casks which are sealed to exclude as much atmospheric moisture as possible.

Cantharidin, when applied to the skin, irritates the kidneys. It penetrates the skin readily, and even in small quantities produces very violent and superficial irritation which results in blistering within a few hours. That may be the reason why in the past "fly blisters" were often used in the treatment of kidney troubles. The dried beetles were pulverized and the powder thus obtained was made into a paste and applied to the skin.

Cantharidin has also been used by the unenlightened as an aphrodisiac. It was the basic ingredient of "love" potions. Swallowed in the quantity necessary to produce appreciable results, it causes severe inflammation of the kidneys and reproductive system, and because its effects are dangerous to life its internal administration has been generally discontinued. It was used for centuries, having been mentioned as an aphrodisiac by Hippocrates. The ancient Romans relied greatly on the excitement derived from swallowing the powdered beetle to sustain them in their orgies. The gladiators punctuated their activities with hot baths which aided in the excretion of the poison from their systems. By this means, they were able to minimize its ill effects.

As far back as Hippocrates, cantharidin was commonly used in the treatment of dropsy. And in Germany, in the time of Frederick the Great, the blister beetle was used as a cure for hydrophobia. In fact, it is recorded that the king paid a large sum of money to the originator of the hydrophobia cure formula. This called for "twenty-five beetles that had been preserved in honey, two drachms of powdered black ebony, one drachm of Virginia snakeroot, and one ditto of lead filings, twenty-five grains of fungus Sorbi—to be reduced to a very fine substance; the whole, with two ounces of theriaca of Venice (and if necessary, a little elder-root) to be formed into an electuary"—and the formula also stipulated that the beetles had to be captured by slipping a hair around their necks, and hung until dry!

Contrary to general belief, the use of cantharidin is not a thing of the past. Reputable pharmacists report steady sales of it as an ingredient of many hair tonics, and veterinarians use it specifically for purposes of breeding. An important present-day use of the beetles is to produce true blisters for relief of various internal inflammations. When applied directly over the seat of the pain the blisters form in about two to three hours, after which the beetles are removed and replaced by a flaxseed poultice.

LUMINOUS BEETLES

Each species of luminous beetle has a distinctive rhythm of flashing —the duration of the glow and the time interval between glowing periods vary according to species. The intensity of the light emitted is governed by the size of the beetle's luminous organ; some appear to emit bright flashes, others seem to glow "softly." Some scientists believe that these beetles may regulate their flashings by regulating the amount of oxygen which reaches the luminous organ. While light, as we know it, is always associated with heat, the light emitted by these insects is a "cold" light, inasmuch as no instruments yet devised have been able to detect any increase in temperature—even when the light organs have been concentrated by thousands under laboratory conditions. This fact has intrigued research men. For a number of years several scientists, and especially Dr. William McElroy of Johns Hopkins University, have encouraged children in their neighborhoods to collect live fireflies by paying about 25¢ per hundred for them. When the fireflies are brought to the laboratory they are put under refrigeration in order to preserve the luminous elements (the enzyme causing the light) for purposes of experiment. Then the luminous organs of hundreds of thousands of these fireflies are mashed. From this mass is isolated the basic luminescent material, the substance which excites it, and the chemical which "triggers" the light-producing reaction in the special cells situated in the lower abdomens of these insects. Dr. McElroy has proved, for the first time, that the "trigger" is the same substance as that by which the contraction of human muscles is brought about. The study of luminous beetles continues, not only in the attempt to find a substance that occurs in nature which can be synthesized to produce a similar effect of "cold" light but, in a much wider sense, to discover the phenomena involved in the release of muscular energy in other animals.

Used for decoration is a luminous beetle variously called the elater, the clickbeetle, or the snapjack (Elateridae). Touching one of them will show that they have been aptly named. The beetle at once curls up its legs, drops to the ground on its back and "plays 'possum." Suddenly, with a click, it propels itself several inches into the air, lands right side up, and scampers off. Throughout the islands, in the West Indies, when ladies go to a ball, they may wear instead of jewels these living, glowing elaterids fastened on their dresses and in their hair by means of pins. For certain festive days the beetles are caught in great numbers and horses' trappings are also decorated, so that on a dark night a procession gives the effect of large numbers of moving lights. If the beetles are to be used on more than one occasion they are kept alive by being fed a little cane sugar, since their luminosity would cease immediately upon death.

These beetles are credited with having played an important role in history. It is recorded that when Sir James Cavendish and Sir Robert Dudley first landed in the West Indies they saw countless numbers of moving lights in the direction of the woods. These were the lights emitted by elater beetles in natural flight, but from a distance the English mistook them for Spaniards advancing upon them with lighted matches and so retired to their ships.

Beetles that are luminous are not confined to the tropics. During warm evenings, beginning in the month of June, tiny spurts of light stabbing the rural darkness are a familiar sight to those living in the north temperate zone of the United States. The characteristic of emitting flashes of light is possessed by the larvae and adults of both sexes of the soft-bodied beetles we call fireflies. They are nocturnal in habit; during daylight hours they are sluggish and hide under leaves. We consider them beneficial because they feed upon other soft-bodied insect pests, such as the aphids.

According to a Chinese legend, this is the origin of the glowworm: Once there was a happy family—a mother, a father, and a son. The mother died and the father married soon thereafter. It was not long before the boy came to fear his stepmother because she was always cruel and unreasonably demanding. One day, she gave him some coppers and ordered him to go to the village beyond the mountain to buy peanut oil—and to return quickly. When the boy reached the village he discovered that he had lost the money, and although he searched for hours, he could not find it. While he was still searching, a storm arose. Because of the storm he lost his way, fell into a stream, and was drowned. But even in death, the fear of his cruel stepmother did not leave him, for his spirit kept repeating: "I must find my coppers! I must find my coppers!" So, the Chinese legend tells us, the spirit of that little boy is the glowworm—an insect carrying a little lamp—searching endlessly for the lost money.

In Japan, fireflies are relegated to the realm of the blessed as ghosts of slain warriors who have won eternal bliss by virtue of having sacrificed their lives for their country. In some regions skilled persons catch fireflies by the thousands to sell to outdoor restaurants and garden parties, where these living, flashing lanterns are released to brighten and beautify the immediate surroundings.

"Keisetsu" is the Japanese word meaning "fireflies and snow," which signifies diligence or hard study. The tradition is that many serious Japanese students have continued to study by the "lanterns" of fireflies and by the light reflected from snow after the sun has set. A superstition differing from the Japanese belief prevails in the Mediterranean region, for there it is thought that the phosphorescent light of fireflies emanates from graves and partakes of a spiritual form. Hence, these insects are very carefully avoided.

In America, when a glowworm appears in an individual's path, it supposedly denotes brilliant success in his undertakings. Country people will admonish one never to kill it, for, they say, "if you kill a glowworm you will put the light out of your house," and by that they mean happiness, prosperity, or whatever blessing one may be enjoying.

SCARABS

To the ancient Egyptians the beetle was a symbol of eternal life, and was held sacred from prehistoric times, as is evidenced by preserved beetles and by images of them carved in such stones as jade, azurite, malachite, green feldspar, obsidian, black steatite, and sometimes in precious stones—usually emeralds. The image, called either a scarab or scarabaeus, symbolized the sun-god Khepera, who was also the "Creator" and the "Father of the Gods" to the Egyptians.

Scarabs were widely used as charms and ornaments, and also served as gifts. When used in burial ceremonies they had particular significance as symbols of resurrection. However, the emphasis on sym-

FIGURE 11. A Heart Scarab Made of Black Steatite Heart scarabs became such an integral part of mortuary beliefs that they were incorporated as part of the death ritual in the Book of the Dead in the early xviiith dynasty (1580–1350 B.C.) A sacred beetle or scarabaeus was cut from stone and inscribed with a charm, usually with the significant words, "O my heart, rise not up against me as witness." This symbol, when so inscribed and placed upon the breast of the mummy, under the wrappings, served to secure exemption from the sins of an evil life as the guilty soul stood before Osiris (the great Egyptian god of the underworld and judge of the dead) in the Judgment Hall. It was considered the means by which the dead triumphed in the hereafter.

bolic significance varied according to dynasties. Usually, after a man died, his heart was removed and a scarab was inserted in its place. Sometimes a half dozen or more scarabs were placed on a mummy, along with the figures of the gods; sometimes the Egyptians painted a likeness of the beetle on the sarcophagus (the outer stone covering inside of which the mummy was placed), and at other times the actual beetle was placed in the tomb. So it came about that an insect was immortalized among men thousands of years ago.

From the habits and structures of this insect the people of Egypt evolved a wonderful symbolism. The beetle itself personified the sun because of the sharp projections on its head, which extended outward like the rays of the sun; it was also a symbol of resurrection and immortality. The five terminal segments on each of the six legs totaled thirty in number and represented the days of the month, since the Egyptian calendar was based upon a thirty-day month. The "ball" which the beetle supposedly rolled from sunrise to sunset represented the earth. Actually, this beetle gathers manure, which it forms or rolls into a ball in order to deposit eggs therein, so that when the eggs hatch the soft inner core of the ball supplies the food needs of the larvae. Of course, sacred scarab beetles were, and still are, nothing more than dung beetles.

All sacred scarab beetles were assumed to be males and to the Egyptians a race of males was a race of warriors. This concept was later carried to Rome where it became the custom for

Roman soldiers to wear images of the sacred scarab beetle set in rings, as talismans. To this day tourists in Egypt wear such rings or send them home as good luck pieces. For centuries it was believed that a scarab carved from a green emerald had the property of rendering the sight more piercing. For this reason it was customary for engravers of precious stones to concentrate their gaze upon the image of the beetle at regular intervals during the day.

Small amulets in beetle form bear the names of kings, of members of royal families, and of officials from early Egyptian dynasties. Frequently they carry a dating which fixes them in Egyptian history, much as coins do in Western history. However, commemorative scarabs of this kind number only a few hundred and make up but a small percentage of the whole group.

At least six different kinds of scarabs resembled living beetles and were venerated and used for their magical properties. The main characteristics of these conventionalized images set them apart according to dynasties. These characteristics are listed here in order of importance.

Scarabaeus sacer—serrated shield on anterior margin of lunate head, xth to xxvth dynasty (2445 B.C. to 633 B.C.)

Scarabaeus venerabilis—ribbed wings, xixth to xxth dynasty (1350 B.C. to 1090 B.C.)

Catharsius—square head, xiith to xvith dynasty (2000 B.C. to 1580 B.C.)

Copris—horned head, xiiith to xvith dynasty (1788 B.C. to 1580 B.C.)

Gymnopleurus—marked side notches on the body turning in above the wings and then downwards, xviiith to xxvith dynasty (1580 B.C. to 525 B.C.)

Hypselogenia—long beak, xiith to xviiith dynasty (2000 B.C. to 1350 B.C.)

Among the Bedouins of Egypt, eating dung beetles is an integral part of the ceremony initiating a boy of eleven or twelve years of age to manhood. The men of the tribe form a circle, within which the boy and the Sheikh take positions. The Sheikh, who holds a Koran, calls out the ninety-nine names of Allah, and as each name is called it is intoned in rhythm by the encircling men. When they have all worked themselves into a religious fervor, the Sheikh commands the boy to eat from a bowl of beetles. The boy obeys the command and thereupon becomes recognized as a man of the tribe or village.

At one time dung beetles were also used medicinally. According to Pliny (Caius Plinius Secundus, an industrious Roman compiler of natural history who lived about 50 A.D.) many Romans carried beetles on their persons by advice of their "magicians"—not "physicians"! The insects were tied in a linen cloth and then attached to the body with a red string as a relief for "quartan ague," which was probably one of the malarial fevers.

FIGURE 12.

The giant of the beetles is the Goliath beetle (*Goliathus goliathus*), native to French Equatorial Africa. There are several species of Goliath beetles and they are usually strikingly marked with white areas on a red-brown to black background. *Goliathus goliathus* measures over six inches in length, is capable of flight when mature, and makes a loud whirring noise as it flies. In spite of its great size it is harmless and the native children search carefully for it in order to use it as a toy. The children tie one end of a string to a stick, and the other end to the neck or leg of this powerful beetle. Then, as the beetle whirs around furiously, it describes an arc the length of the string.

In South America there are species of metallic-green leaf-eating beetles that are utilized in decorative objects because of their beauty, durability, and characteristic retention of natural coloring and lustre without the application of artificial preservatives. The natives fashion necklaces and headdresses with them, and a small quantity is exported to this country where they are made into cufflinks. Only the hard front wing-covers are used for necklaces but for headdresses and cufflinks the whole beetles are employed.

In Wales there is a superstition that a smaller beetle of this same family supposedly foretells the direction from which the future husband of a fair maiden will come. The lady places one of these beetles on her extended hand and then observes the direction of its flight. The belief is that sooner or later from that quarter will arrive the man of her dreams.

LADYBUGS

Memories of childhood are brought back to almost every American by the familiar couplet:

> Ladybug, ladybug, fly away home,
> Your house is on fire, your children will burn.

Just where this couplet originated has always been a question. It is based upon the fact that the young of the ladybug (or ladybird) beetle feed upon soft-bodied insect pests such as plant lice (aphids), mealybugs, and scale insects infesting hop vines. After the hops were harvested it was customary to burn the vines. This cleared the field for the next planting and at the same time destroyed the insect pests. However, it also destroyed the young of the ladybug that were on the vines because young ladybugs are wingless and unable to fly.

Many years ago citrus fruit orchards in California were being attacked by mealybugs, plant lice, and scale insects, and the use of various insecticidal sprays did not bring them under control. However, it was known that ladybug beetles and their larvae greedily devoured these crop destroyers. In fact, only ten adult ladybug beetles and their offspring can free a badly infested tree of these bugs within a few months. So in 1892 a species of beetle was imported from Australia to help combat these pests. This was *Rhodolia cardinalis*, which became the most famous ladybug beetle in the entomological world because this was the first successful introduction into any country of a beneficial insect that preyed upon injurious ones and is, therefore, a standard example of biological control. It did its job so well that it almost died out because of lack of food, and it has become necessary for the State of California Insectary to propagate ladybugs artificially from year to year in order to insure a supply.

Some years later, *Hippodamia convergens*, a species native to North America, was also found to have a voracious appetite for mealybugs, plant lice, and scale insects. It was discovered that as adults they have a unique habit of congregating on mountain tops where they hibernate for the winter. When this discovery was made it became a commercial undertaking, each fall, for Californians to collect these beetles by the ton and place them in cold storage for the winter. In the spring, when crop pest insects made their appearance, the ladybugs were taken out of storage and placed in orchards where they thawed out and *presumably* went to work immediately. Now the practice of collecting and storing these beetles is diminishing, because the theory that they started to feed immediately after thawing out was found to have a flaw in it. One of the fundamental facts about the migrating habit of these insects had been overlooked. It has now been established that when these insects emerge from their hibernation, their first and overpowering instinct is the retracing of a flight distance equal to that covered by their migratory flight to the mountain top. Therefore, when prematurely released in an orchard, weeks before they would have normally come out of hibernation on the mountain top, they fly away as soon as they thaw out. Thus, someone else's orchard may get early protection against insect pests, but not necessarily the same person who has spent the money for the "cold storage" beetles.

According to an ancient record, ladybug beetles had another practical use. They were once prescribed as an excellent remedy for colic and measles. Another old record tells how ladybugs were used to cure a toothache: "One or two were mashed and stuffed into the cavity of the tooth." Accounts actually exist attesting to the efficacy of this cure.

As familiar as the gurgling brook to the country rover are the steel-blue or black whirligig beetles that are found gyrating in masses on the surface of relatively still water, or basking like turtles on logs or stones. When danger appears they catch a bubble of air under a wing-cover and dive deeply under the surface, where they can remain until danger is past. Although they spend most of their active time in the surface of the water they fly well and dive freely. Like the bugs known as water gliders or striders, whirligigs can "walk" over the water. This characteristic is due to their lightness, and also to their ability to keep from breaking through the surface film of still water. There is always a surface film, or tension, on water. As long as this tension is not broken the insect is able to maintain its buoyancy. (This is much the same as resting an oil-coated needle on still water— the needle will float. If the surface tension is broken by agitation, or if it is altered by the addition of a detergent, the needle will sink.) These whirligig beetles are commonly called "lucky bugs" or "dollar bugs," but they are also known as scuttle bugs, penny bugs, eel bugs, mellow bugs, sugar bugs, and water fleas. John D. Godman, author of "Rambles of a Naturalist," said in 1830 that the boys called these whirligigs "water-witches" and "apple-smellers" and that they have a delightful odor, similar to that of the richest, mellowest apple. In eastern Massachusetts it is believed that the capture of a "lucky bug" is a sign of coming good fortune, providing you "bury it and make a wish—then your wish will come true."

On the debit side of the ledger, beetles are great destroyers of man's possessions—such as his crops, his wooden furniture, woolen clothing, leather goods, provisions in the larder—indeed, the very beams that support the structure of his house. Most of the damage is done by the well-adapted mouthparts which beetles possess during the larval stage, at which time they eat or bore their way through material in their constant search for food.

The Tahltan Indians of western British Columbia account for the wood-boring beetle with the following myth: A long time ago Wormwood (the larvae of a beetle) and Mosquito lived together. Day after day Wormwood saw his companion, Mosquito, come home swollen with blood that he had eaten. When questioned, Mosquito, not wishing to give away his secret, replied that he had sucked it out of the trees. Wormwood immediately attacked the trees, and to this day he and his descendants bore into wood looking for blood. If Wormwood had been told the truth, instead of attacking trees he now would be attacking man.

This habit of boring is the basis for one of the most widespread beliefs existing among people who live in rural communities—that death generally announces its coming by a mysterious noise in the house, referred to as the "death-watch" or "death-tick." Many persons who recognize this mysterious ticking noise as the click of a beetle in the walls of a house say that it is the mating call of the beetle —which may or may not be true. Others say the ticking noise associated with this superstition of impending death is really caused by the beetle when it butts its loosely jointed head against its burrow as it bores its way through the timbers. Some think that this noise is made by a tiny, whitish, wingless insect known as a book louse. However, it is not probable that a soft-bodied insect $\frac{1}{25}$ of an inch long can produce sounds audible to human ears.

In medieval times a prelate known as "the witty Dean of Saint Patrick" tried to erase this superstition from the minds of the people by ridiculing the idea in a song about a cobbler in a stall. It runs thus:

A wood worm
That lies in old wood, like a hare in her form,
With teeth or with claws, it will bite, it will scratch;
And chambermaids christen this worm a Death-watch;
Because like a watch, it always cries click.

Then woe be to those in the house that are sick!
For, sure as a gun, they will give up the ghost,
If the maggot cries click when it scratches the post.

But a kettle of scalding hot water injected,
Infallibly cures the timber affected:
The omen is broken, the danger is over,
The maggot will die, and the sick will recover.

MISCELLANEOUS

PROVERBS:

"He sees a glowworm and thinks it a conflagration."
"The beetle is a thing of beauty in the eyes of its mother."

GENERAL:

If on the gold beetle's wings more than seven black spots are found, the corn harvest will be scanty; if less than seven the harvest will be unusually abundant.

If the seed is sown after sunset or before sunrise, flea beetles will not infest the plants.

Cucumbers were regarded as infallible in driving vermin away.—"Put the shells of seed cucumbers into the granary and they will drive out the weevils."

A ladybug will bring money and to kill one is unlucky.

If a firefly comes into the house, on the following day there will be one person more or one person less in that house.

When a lightning bug comes into the house, be sure that an old friend will visit.

If a snapjack or click beetle enters your house a quarrel will ensue which may end in blows.

If fire from the firefly gets into the eye, it will put it out.

If you take a bess bug (a wood-boring beetle, *Passalus cornutus*) and cut off its head, one drop of blood will flow. This will cure earache.

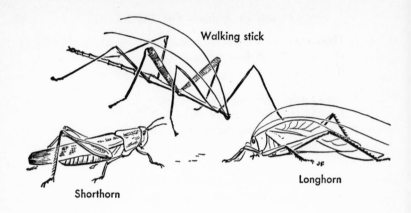

Walking stick

Shorthorn

Longhorn

Chapter IV

"Archie" the Cockroach, and His Relatives

As we have seen, the Order Lepidoptera includes only the insects commonly known as moths and butterflies, and the Order Coleoptera includes only the insects commonly known as beetles. However, the Order Orthoptera is a zoological classification that includes a tremendous variety of insects. Among them are primitive cockroaches which are very much like their ancestors that roamed the earth as early as the Carboniferous period, some 250,000,000 years ago; grotesque looking walking sticks; praying mantids and leaf insects; leaping grasshoppers and burrowing mole crickets; katydids that live in tree tops and roadside grasshoppers that frequent dusty roads; meadow grasshoppers that inhabit the grass jungles, and cave crickets that live in dark, cool, damp places. Members of this order move about by leaping, crawling, running, flying, or burrowing, and some orthopteran is usually present where man works, plays, or lives—whether it be indoors or outdoors.

The insects belonging to the first two orders go through what is known as complete metamorphosis during their life cycles—the young bearing no resemblance to their parents.   But in the case of Orthoptera, metamorphosis is incomplete—the young can be identified for what they are, immediately upon hatching.

Orthopterans are essentially terrestrial insects even though some species fly for miles on migratory journeys.   Sometimes the wings are reduced or entirely lost, but when wings are present they are intricately veined and there are four in number.   The front pair, from which the name of the order is derived, is comparatively straight.   (Orthoptera: *orthos* = straight; *ptera* = wings).   They are also longer and narrower than the hind membranous wings which are used in flight, and serve to cover and protect the hind wings when the insect is at rest.   These hind wings are much larger in area than most people realize, for the reason that when folded—in a manner that may be likened to a folded fan when completely closed—they rest compactly against the body.

The more familiar sounds of the summertime are made by members of this order.   The production of sound is almost always confined to the males, and the music is instrumental and not vocal as among the birds.   The grasshoppers, katydids, and crickets, bear their "musical instruments" externally, on their legs or on their wings.   They may produce "music" while hovering over the fields, or while they rest, by rubbing tooth-like projections on the underside of one wing against a rough area on the upper side of the other wing.   This is a true fiddling action.

In the case of a species of wingless katydid, *Stenopelmatus longispina*, the hind legs have developed rasps on the inner surface that play against the short teeth or tubercules projecting from the body.   In addition to making its characteristic sound, this unusual katydid can make its joints squeak while walking.

The insects in the Order Orthoptera are large in size compared with most insects in other orders, and some of them are among the giants of their class—like the four-inch tropical cockroach, the South American grasshopper that reaches a length of approximately five inches, and the Walking Stick from the Malay Peninsula (the longest insect known) which has reached a length of thirteen inches.

COCKROACHES

Blattidae, better known as cockroaches, are sometimes called water bugs or black beetles. Although cockroaches rank among the most primitive of winged insects, their present-day appearance presents very little change from their ancestral fossil forms. And while it may be news to many people, most adult cockroaches can fly. Linnaeus, the scientist who first named them, was so struck by their aversion to light

that he chose the word *"Blatta"* to set them apart from all other insects. Translated from the Latin, *Blatta* indicates an "insect that shuns the light," as anyone who has seen them scampering from a sudden beam of light well knows. Although cockroaches are omnivorous, they ruin far more by fouling than they actually consume.

FIGURE 13.

Cockroaches abound in human habitations throughout the world. It is practically impossible to be free of them where there are multiple dwellings, no matter how clean a home may be. Once on the premises they work their way through small openings, usually following water pipes for they are attracted to moist places. Under city conditions they would not normally come in contact with disease organisms, but where there is improper sewerage disposal they could, after coming in contact with fecal matter, subsequently walk over food and thus mechanically deposit disease organisms. However, of themselves, cockroaches have not been incriminated as disease-disseminators.

There are three periods in the life of "Archie" as the cockroach is endearingly referred to in humorous literature. His mother drops the eggs—anywhere at all—enclosed in a protective capsule. The second step takes place within a few hours when the egg-capsule splits open along the seam, revealing two rows of roaches facing each other. They may total from 12 to over 40 roaches, according to the species. As the insects swell themselves with air, the capsule opens wider and wider. The last period finds "Archie" emerged from his egg and from that moment he is entirely on his own. Immediately after hatching, he is whitish and soft, but upon contact with the air his body-covering soon hardens and changes to brown. He has about a week to make good because he can live that long without food. Although a week is the accepted time that a young cockroach can sustain himself, an adult roach can live considerably longer. A full-grown South American cockroach, in the possession of the author, actually lived without food for a period of seven and a half months before it died. However, it had access to and did drink water.

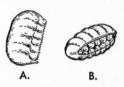

A.　　　　**B.**

To emphasize the adaptability of cockroaches in taking up residence in human habitation, they have now moved into one of man's latest acquisitions in the home. In recent years, when exterminators go out on a job, their boss's parting shot is: "Look out for the TV roach." The "TV roach" (*Supella supellectilium*), commonly known as the brown-banded roach, is a species of cockroach native to East Africa which somehow got to Cuba, then to Florida, and now is well established, particularly in the New York City area. It lives in TV sets, feeding on paste, glue, insulation, etc., and does not come out like other household cockroaches to look for food in the pantry. In its cozy TV home it has the darkness which it likes, and the tubes provide the heat. Where do these insects get water? In all probability this is a species of cockroach that metabolizes water, as do other insects such as some that live in deserts and in dry grain; their own bodies have the ability to produce water molecules from the food they eat. There is, of course, no basis for the common superstition that cockroaches generate spontaneously from bread crumbs and other food left lying about.

FIGURE 14. A. Egg capsule showing resemblance to a closed purse. **B.** Egg capsule partially opened by roaches which are about to emerge.

Cockroaches in one form or another have been considered by some people to be an important ingredient for special medicines. The Indians of Jamaica drink a mixture containing the ashes of cockroaches as a cure for certain diseases, and also administer it to their children to kill worms. Mashed with sugar, cockroaches are applied to ulcers and cancers as a healing aid.

One of the common large species of roach has been used in Russia for dropsy. It apparently was given in the form of the powdered insect as well as in various other ways. In that country the medicine was known as "Tarakané," and on the continent it was sold commercially as "Pulvis Tarakanae."

In the *New York Times* of January 3, 1886, under the title "The Creole Doctor," Lafcadio Hearn wrote entertainingly of the curious medical beliefs of Louisiana Negroes. Among the various remedies for diverse ills, mention is made of cockroach tea for tetanus (lockjaw), supplemented by a poultice of boiled cockroaches over the wound. He mentioned that cockroaches fried in oil with garlic are good for indigestion! It is also said in Louisiana that if cockroaches run around the house a storm is on the way.

Superstition is one of the greatest handicaps encountered by scientific workers who are trying to wipe out tropical disease in the jungles of the Upper Amazon. In the *New York Times* of November 12, 1944, the following report appeared: "The changing of living habits necessary to this part of the program is extremely difficult among people of low cultural and economic level. Interesting superstitions and beliefs are legion, as are many quack methods of treatment. For example, during an epidemic of influenza in Iquitos [a city in Peru] one of the most commonly used remedies was an infusion of red Iquitos cockroaches [a local variety of cockroach] steeped in a particularly potent variety of 'pisco' (a fiery Peruvian liquor named after the town of its origin)."

Dr. Samuel X. Radbill in his paper on "Child Hygiene among the American Indians" (1945), states that among the methods used to avert or cure whooping cough was one that involved the use of cockroaches. As many cockroaches were collected as there were children afflicted with whooping cough. Then each cockroach was named after a child and each child placed his roach in a bottle and kept it tightly corked. When the roach died the sickness was believed to disappear. During this period, as part of the charm, the child was dosed with cathartics.

As a remedy to rid a house of cockroaches, from Springfield, Massachusetts, came the following superstition: Catch a roach, put it in a piece of paper with a small amount of money, give the parcel to anyone who will take it and the cockroaches will go to the house of the person who accepts the parcel.

GRASSHOPPERS

The representatives of the Order Orthoptera which are remarkable for their leaping powers, are the grasshoppers. Grasshoppers, katydids, and locusts are generally all "grasshoppers" to the layman, which is perfectly understandable because they have many characteristics in common and bear a close resemblance to each other. They *are* different species of insects, although only a taxonomist can tell them apart. Since they have always been commonly called "grasshoppers," except by the professional entomologist, this practice will be continued in the following pages.

There are short-horned grasshoppers, so called because their antennae are heavy and very short. The locusts belong in this short-horned grasshopper group, but unfortunately the term locust has also been applied to the cicada—with considerable resultant confusion. The cicada, commonly known as the seventeen-year locust, is really a bug. It will be discussed later under the Order Hemiptera.

There are also long-horned grasshoppers, so named because their long, slender antennae are much longer than their bodies. The katydids belong in this long-horned grasshopper group.

The male katydid is among the most musical of the grasshoppers and many have pondered upon the oft-repeated debate as to whether "Katy did" or "Katy didn't." To account for the singular sound produced by the katydid, a curious legend is told in Virginia and Maryland. This was put into verse by Mrs. A. L. Dufour in 1864:

> Two maiden sisters loved a gallant youth,
>   Once in the far-off days of olden time:
> With all of women's fervency and truth;—
>   So runs a very ancient rhyme.

Blanche, chaste and beauteous as a Fairy-queen,
 Brave Oscar's heart a willing captive led;
Lovely in soul as was her form and mien,
 While guileless love its light around her shed.

A Juno was the proud and regal Kate,—
 Her love thus scorned, her beauty thus defied,
Like Juno's turned her love to vengeful hate:—
 Mysteriously the gallant Oscar died.

Bereft of reason, faithful Blanche soon lay;—
 The mystery of this fearful fate none knew,
Save proud, revengeful Kate, who would not say
 It was her hand had dared the deed to do.

Justice and pity then to Jove appealed,
 That the dark secret be no longer hid;
Young Oscar's spirit he at once concealed,
 That cries, each summer night, Kate Katy-did!

The katydid usually does not start to sing until near the end of the summer, because this insect must be fully developed before it can use its wings to produce sound. The Cherokee Indians associate the music of the katydid with the ripening of corn and the end of the summer, and say "Katydid has brought the roasting ear-bread." Throughout the United States it is generally believed that after the first katydid is heard frost is only six weeks off.

How the first grasshopper was created is told in the following Greek myth. Once upon a time, Aurora, Goddess of the Morning, fell in love with a hunter—a mortal by the name of Tithonus. Tithonus in turn fell so madly in love with Aurora that he eagerly consented to forsake his land of mortals to live with her in the land of the gods. For some time they were very happy together, until Aurora became disturbed by the thought that Tithonus, being a mortal, would some-day die. She confided her fears to him, explaining that his death was inevitable unless she could get her father, the King of the Gods, to confer immortality upon him. Thereupon she went to her father and persuaded him to make Tithonus immortal. But, in her wish, Aurora forgot to ask her father to confer perpetual youth on Tithonus. Too late came the realization that while Aurora had remained young and beautiful, Tithonus had grown much older in appearance. This made Tithonus so sad that he finally asked Aurora to be allowed to return to the land of the mortals. Realizing his unhappiness she finally released him, but as she did she said: "From now on you shall be a grasshopper so that whenever I hear the grasshopper's clear, merry song, I shall be reminded of the many happy days we spent together."

The migratory locust is probably the most celebrated grasshopper. Since biblical times all the devastations of crops have been attributed to it, and in the tenth chapter of Exodus the destructive ability of the locust is described in the following manner: "They went up all over the land of Egypt and rested in all the coasts of Egypt: very grievous were they for they did eat every herbe of the land."

Locusts have plagued man ever since his first attempts at farming. In the early days such attacks were attributed to the devil and conjurers were called upon to break up swarms. Attempts were also made to drive them away by burning sulphur in the plazas, to frighten them with church bells, drums, bugles, cannons, or huge bonfires.

In the mid-twenties Mexicans were required to use a stamp called a "locust" in addition to the regular ten centavos stamp used on letters. This "locust" was an extra one centavo stamp that the government had decreed must appear on all first-class mail. The proceeds went into a national fund for combating locusts that were causing great trouble by their depredations in the southwestern states of Mexico. The battle against these insect hordes failed because new hordes crossed the border from Guatemala. By 1934 both Mexico and Guatemala decided to unite their forces in their common problem and signed a joint agreement to try to eradicate the insects. Even this was found to be ineffective when it was discovered that the swarms originated in countries farther to the south, such as El Salvador, Nicaragua, and Costa Rica. The problem continued to be of importance and in 1947 ministers of the five central American countries and Mexico met in San Salvador. As a result of this meeting international extermination campaigns were initiated in 1949 and 1950, and by 1951 the invasions seemed to have stopped.

Migratory locusts sometimes travel enormous distances. Clouds of them have been seen over the Atlantic up to 1200 miles from land.

The locusts that invaded England in 1869 apparently originated along the east coast of Africa. One swarm in 1639 took three days to pass over Lisbon, and another swarm, sighted in 1889, which was crossing the Red Sea was calculated to have covered an area of two thousand square miles.

There are many species of true locusts that may be considered as migratory. The species occurring in east and central Russia, Africa, west Asia, and Europe is the migratory locust *Locusta migratoria*. Another species found in Africa, Arabia, Palestine, Syria, Persia and west India is known as the desert locust (*Schistocerca gregaria*). There are also the Moroccan locust, the South American locust, the brown locust, the red locust, and the Rocky Mountain locust—all true migratory locusts.

Grasshoppers are great destroyers of food, yet they have been captured in great numbers and used *as* food. In fact it is recorded that their abundance in certain sections has actually been the means of preventing famine. Grasshoppers have always been a widespread article of food in countries of the Far East. In the list of things the Jews were permitted to eat (Leviticus XI, 22) there seems to be a distinction between locusts and grasshoppers. Since there is considerable confusion in even the present usage of these terms, it is rather hopeless to attempt a definite determination of what the ancient writers had in mind.

The belief that John the Baptist ate locusts is disputed by Ralph D. Cornell in an article in the *New York Herald-Tribune* of July 3, 1943. According to Mr. Cornell, "The locusts eaten by John the Baptist while he was dressed in camel's hair at the River Jordan, were not grasshoppers or locusts but simply the pods of the carob tree." Mr. Cornell says translators confused the honey locust tree, which has pods like the carob, with the insect itself. Therefore, John, instead of devouring the migratory locust, was actually eating the fruit of the carob tree— or St. John's bread.

In one of the numerous handbooks published by our armed forces during World War II, *cooked* grasshoppers were recommended as food in case of emergency. Cooking them first was made SOP (Standard Operating Procedure) in order to destroy the parasites that are harbored by some of these insects. This really was a safety measure against the possibility of grasshopper parasites being harmful to man, even though it has not been established that such parasites could be successfully transmitted to man and live within his body.

A grasshopper roast once was one of the choice meals of the California Digger Indians. Feasts were held during the seasons when these insects appeared in swarms. After being collected, the grasshoppers were soaked in salt water for a few minutes and then put into ovens and roasted for about fifteen minutes. They were eaten immediately upon being removed from the ovens, or they were crushed into a powder from which a soup could be made for later consumption. It has been claimed that devastations caused by the Rocky Mountain grasshoppers never attained the present-day magnitude when the Indians of North America collected them in the great numbers necessary for their feasts.

As a child, do you remember catching a grasshopper, holding it very gently between your fingers, and saying: "Chew tobacco, chew tobacco, spit, spit, spit!", and then waiting for the grasshopper to exude a drop of dark fluid? Children believe this dark fluid possesses wart-curing qualities.

In China, and in Japan also, this fluid was preserved for medicinal uses and sold in apothecary shops.

Among the ancient Athenians the grasshopper was a favorite symbol and because of the high esteem in which it was held it was considered very unlucky to kill one.

In a fable of gentle tone but unmistakable intent, Aesop tells the story of the futile attempt of the grasshopper to divert the ant from her labors by an invitation to chat. In the winter the grasshopper, dying of hunger, had learned too late that "It is best to prepare for the days of necessity."

CRICKETS

The insects commonly called crickets are very closely related to the grasshoppers and the locusts. There is a "field" cricket which is dark brown to black, and there is a "house" cricket which is usually very much lighter in color. The house cricket is particularly fond of warmth and thus frequently is found near the hearth and in bake shops.

Their liking for warmth has led to the belief, in Virginia and Maryland, that crickets are "old folks" and therefore should not be destroyed. Their sudden departure from a hearth which has long echoed with their chirping is often regarded as the worst thing that could happen to that family, for the belief is that it betokens approaching misfortune. The presence of house crickets is considered an omen of prosperity and the idea is widespread that to kill one is to invite trouble.

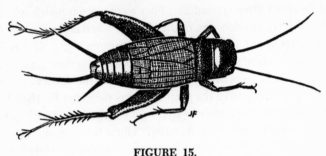

FIGURE 15.

In Maine it is thought that if a cricket is caught in a deep crevice in the rock, or between boards, the bystander who does not release it will suffer bad luck.

In Malay it is believed that the spirits of the dead assume a form that is recognizable, the best known of these taking the shape of a house cricket. This superstition takes on added interest when compared with the belief in Virginia and Maryland that house crickets are "old folks." It is another definite instance emphasizing the sameness of certain beliefs throughout the world, even among peoples of different cultures.

The Cherokee Indians call the cricket "tălátú," meaning "barber," because of its habit of gnawing hair from furs. For this reason when a Cherokee meets a man with his hair clipped unevenly, a common saying is: "Did the cricket cut your hair?"

The mole cricket (*Gryllotalpa*) owes its name to the striking resemblance in its structure and habits to the common mole. It is equipped with hand-like claws adapted for digging and tunneling. The Cherokees call it "gûl 'kwâgĭ," literally meaning "seven" (probably because of the possession of seven fingerlike projections on the front, digging legs.)   They repute it to be alert, hard to catch, and an excellent singer that never makes mistakes.   It plays an important part in preparing the Cherokee Indians for the duties of life.   If an infant is slow in learning to speak, his tongue is scratched with the claw of a living mole cricket.   The insect is held in the hand of an elder while the operation is performed.   The belief is that this will endow the child with intelligence, with speech that is clear and eloquent, and with the ability to remember without effort.

The Cherokees also believe that with a little more difficulty the same results may be obtained with a grown person, usually a "warrior." The warrior remains in bed for four days, permitting the inside of his throat to be scratched with the claws of a live mole cricket on each successive morning.   This ceremony is performed by the Medicine Man, who pushes the live insect down the warrior's throat with his fingers, and withdraws it the same way.

Another method resorted to by these Indians to get the same results is the placing of the cricket in a bowl of water overnight.   Then, providing the cricket is still alive in the morning, it is taken out and the water is given to the Cherokee to drink.   If the cricket is dead, the water is considered to lack magical power and therefore is not drunk.   In that case another cricket is caught and the performance is repeated.   As the chances are against the cricket being alive the next morning, the ceremony may last for several days before it succeeds. For the period during which the ceremony is in progress tribal taboos are strictly observed as further propitiation for success.   The last act, and an essential one, is to set the cricket free.

In China, cricket fighting is as popular as cock fighting in other parts of the world, and large sums of money are wagered upon these combats. The fighting crickets receive special attention and special food consisting of rice mixed with fresh cucumbers, boiled chestnuts, lettuce, seeds, and mosquitoes.   Prior to a tournament they are either fed a tonic or else starved in order to get them in a ferocious mood.   Cricket ticklers, made from rat or hare whiskers inserted in reed or ivory handles, are used to incite the insects to fight.   Before a fight, great care is exercised to match crickets so that they are of the same size and weight, because there are heavy, middleweight, and lightweight classes. A pair of extremely small scales is used to weigh in the contestants before each bout begins, and this "weighing in" is done in full view of the spectators. The losing cricket in such a contest pays the supreme penalty; they fight to the death. These fighting crickets are of the field-cricket variety, selected for their "aggressiveness." The average price range for one of these "fighters" is from $50.00 to $100.00. Great sums of money are sometimes wagered in "Championship Contests" and it is stated that the backers of a famous fighting cricket of Canton, named Ghengis Khan, won as much as $90,000 on a single bout.

In China, the chirp of the cricket is greatly admired, and males (for only the males sing) are caught and kept in cages made of bamboo, or in gourds which are especially grown for this purpose. Many Chinese breed crickets in their homes, sometimes devoting several rooms to jars in which crickets are kept. People of wealth often go to the expense of employing a cricket expert to do nothing else but look after their crickets.

FIGURE 16. Chinese Cricket Accessories Left: Cricket tickler used for stimulating crickets to sing or fight. They are usually made from rat or hare whiskers inserted in ivory, bone or reed handles.

Top center and right: Bamboo cricket cages.

Bottom center: A gourd in which crickets are kept. The cover is of ivory and intricately carved.

Since the activity of an insect is dependent upon temperature, it is not surprising to find that the intensity and rate of a cricket's chirp changes with the temperature—increasing at a higher temperature and decreasing at a lower temperature. Based upon the chirps of a field cricket, a formula has been worked out by which the temperature can be closely determined: Count the number of chirps in fifteen seconds and add thirty-eight. The answer will approximate the temperature of the ordinary Fahrenheit scale. Or, the number of chirps per minute can be similarly determined, if the temperature is known, by multiplying the temperature by four and subtracting one hundred and sixty. Over fifty years ago Professor A. E. Dolbear worked out a method of determining temperature by the number of chirps per minute of the snowy tree cricket, but his formula is extremely complicated. A recent researcher makes this seem like a simpler problem by maintaining that temperature may be determined from the chirps of the snowy tree cricket by just counting the number of chirps in fourteen seconds and adding forty-two! The insects commonly called "tree crickets" are said to indicate the approximate temperature if one counts the number of chirps in seven seconds and then adds forty-six.

Only one instance has been found where crickets are eaten. This is in Mandalay where a large brown cricket, which they call *Payit*, is fried and sold in the markets. When placed on sale they are called Payit-kyaw (fried cricket) and are purchased in large quantities by the wealthy Burmese to feed the Hypoongyis (the wandering Buddhist monks).

MANTIDS

Mantids are insects that are very striking in appearance. They may be seen in most regions of the United States, in certain parts of Canada, and in other countries as well, but they are most common in the tropics. Of the fourteen described species now in this country three are exotic, having been introduced quite by accident. These three alien species, which have become well established in the northeastern part of our country, are the narrow-winged mantid, the European mantid, and the Chinese mantid. The Chinese mantid attracts the most attention since it is the largest, attaining a length of four to five inches, and one cannot help but notice it during the months of August and September especially, when it has matured and is capable of flight.

It is generally believed that Chinese

FIGURE 17.

mantids were imported for the express purpose of destroying Japanese beetles, but this is a mistaken notion.   They were accidentally introduced on nursery stock about the year 1895, and while they will eat Japanese beetles if they come across them, they do not prefer them particularly.   Our native species are small by comparison with these foreign species and are confined to the southern half of the United States.

The mantid is generally known as "the praying mantis," "the soothsayer," and "the devil's rearhorse," and because of the characteristic praying pose is looked upon in many parts of the world as being devout.   The word "mantis" is of Greek origin and signifies "diviner."   The Arabs and the Turks believe it prays constantly with its face turned toward Mecca.

In the South the mantid is said to kill or poison livestock, but this too is a mistaken notion for it is harmless, except to other insects—it does not eat plants.   Although it is best known as the "praying" mantis, actually "preying" mantis would be a more fitting name for it since it is the outstanding cannibal in the insect world.   "He eats them alive" and makes no exceptions, even of members of the immediate family!

MISCELLANEOUS

PROVERBS:

"The cockroach is always wrong when arguing with the chicken."
"Cockroaches never get justice when a chicken is the judge."
"Knee high to a grasshopper." (Said of a very small person.)
"It is useless stretching the grasshopper's leg."
"Hold on, wait for the grasshopper." (Meaning "better times.")
"Sound as a roach." [This proverbial expression supposedly is derived from the attributes of Saint Roche—the esteemed Saint of all those afflicted with plague. Although plague was a disease of common occurrence in England about 1664, it was not then known that rats, and the fleas associated with them, were responsible for plague. Instead, people offered prayers to the miraculous Saint Roche, believing that he could make them as "sound as himself."]

GENERAL BELIEFS:

Cockroaches will gnaw one's toe-nails at night unless the feet are well covered by the bed clothes.

If a black beetle (roach) enters your room or flies against you, severe illness or perhaps death will follow.

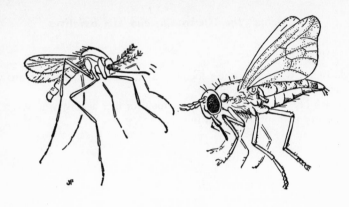

Chapter V

Doggers of Civilization

The Flies

FLIES IN GENERAL

Flies are represented by numerous species distributed throughout the world. The best known are the mosquitoes, gnats, midges, stableflies, horseflies, beeflies, the tsetse flies of Africa, and the houseflies found wherever man has established himself.

The word "fly" also forms a part of many compound names of insects, such as "butterfly," "mayfly," "dragonfly," and "firefly," but these particular insects and others that have *two* pairs of flying wings are not true flies. The true flies are distinguished by possession of *one* pair of flying wings, and this is the characteristic responsible for the name of the Order: Diptera (*di* = two; *ptera* = wings). True flies also possess a pair of tiny, knobbed organs called "halteres" or "balancers," which are really remnants of wings that were fully developed in an earlier evolutionary era.

The hum associated with the flight of all flies varies with the speed of their wing beats, which means that the rapidity of their wing beats is responsible for the sound they produce—a soft or loud, low or high-pitched hum. Studies that have been made on the hum of mosquitoes show that, when amplified one hundred million times, the female mating call sounds like a movie version of a dive bomber shriek. The male's answer is in a distinctly higher pitch. The bluebottle fly, which is larger than the housefly, has a slower wing beat and hums in a distinctly lower key. The housefly hums in the key of F, in the middle octave, and its wing beats equal 345 strokes per second or 20,700 wing beats per minute.

Some flies move very fast. In fact the male deer-botfly (*Cephenomyia pratti*) is reputed to be the fastest animal on wings, some authorities actually claiming that this insect develops a speed of several hundred miles per hour. However, regardless of claims which may be exaggerated, certain species normally travel more than fifty miles per hour, which is a real feat for such small, light, and fragile creatures.

The eggs of flies vary greatly in form and are usually laid in large numbers wherever sufficient food is present. They are even laid in pools of petroleum and some flies actually breed in this medium. When fly eggs hatch into larval forms they are commonly known as "maggots." The maggots pass a concealed life. They may burrow in the tissues of plants, in soil, in decaying refuse, in dung, and even in the bodies of living or dead insects or other animals.

The mouthparts of flies are very complicated and exhibit various modifications involving suctorial organs. These may be of the piercing or non-piercing type and vary according to species, usually being adapted to specific food needs. For instance, the common housefly has a sponging type of mouthpart that is well suited for taking liquid food such as milk, syrup, water, and moisture from decaying fruits and fecal wastes, through a sievelike arrangement at the tip of its proboscis. When the food is not moist, such as a lump of sugar, the housefly can dissolve it by regurgitating the contents of its crop, leaving vomit spots which are commonly referred to as "fly specks." In piercing mouthparts, the piercing may be performed by means of tubelike or hypodermiclike parts as in the case of the mosquito and the stablefly, or by means of bladelike cutting structures, as in the case of the horsefly. So far as is known, mature flies do not chew solid foods and few, if any, pierce plants in order to suck the sap.

Flies are of service to man in many ways. They effect pollination when frequenting flowers for nectar. In this respect no other group of insects is so important to mankind except the bees and wasps belonging to the Order Hymenoptera. Flies are important as scavengers also, rapidly disposing of decaying animal and vegetable matter, and they are of service too by destroying or feeding upon harmful insects.

During the past few decades, insects, and flies in particular, have furnished the material on which a considerable part of our knowledge of heredity is based. This has been of vital interest to plant and animal breeders who seek specific, detailed knowledge of the inheritance of physical and mental traits. To Professor Thomas Hunt Morgan and his students at Columbia University is due the credit of opening up this new field of genetic research, based upon exhaustive studies of the hereditary constitution of a tiny fly known as the fruit-fly (*Drosophila*). This insect presents the advantage of being easily handled—thousands can be reared in little space and require a minimum of care. In addition, the fact that this fly will complete a generation in about ten days means that the geneticist can compile as much data on as many different generations and crosses as he can possibly study during his lifetime. Previous to the discovery of the suitability of the tiny *Drosophila* for this work, heavy expenditures were involved for feed, cages, and caretakers when working with the usual laboratory animals such as rats, rabbits, guinea pigs, etc., but more serious was the limited number of generations that one scientist could rear for study. The twentieth century has witnessed an enormous amount of research in genetics and the fruitfly has been the clue to many of the mysteries of heredity.

However, a war of extermination is relentlessly carried on against Diptera that suck blood and that are associated with the transmission of disease organisms. These are flies such as the horsefly, tsetse fly, deer-botfly, and certain species of mosquitoes. Malaria, sleeping sickness, yellow fever, and other diseases would be impossible of transmission without these intermediary agents. The flies that feed on blood but are not yet known to be disease carriers, such as the stablefly, merely irritate or annoy man by their incessant biting.

MOSQUITOES

Mosquitoes may lay their eggs in rafts of several hundred or they may deposit them singly or in small groups.   In their larval form they are commonly known as "wigglers," a name suggested by the wiggling motion as they swim through the water.   During this developing stage wigglers are without legs.

Mosquitoes must have water in which to complete their life cycles. The water may be in a pond, in a rain barrel, or it may be only a puddle that resulted from a rainstorm and will disappear within a few days. There are even certain species of woodland mosquitoes which are in the habit of breeding in rain water that collects in the cavities of trees. The entire life cycle of a mosquito may take place within a few days, or over as long a period of time as several years.   In the latter category are certain species of mosquitoes associated with floods.   Eggs are laid at the high water level and do not hatch until there is a recurrence of flood waters—an event which may not take place again for several years.   The eggs remain capable of sustaining life and hatch in great numbers immediately upon being moistened by the rising water.

Among the mosquitoes, the female is more deadly than the male. The male mosquito is quite inoffensive; his mouthparts are rudimentary, and his food is confined to the nectar of flowers.   Not so with the female, however.   She is out for blood!   The female mosquito pierces the skin of man or of other animals with a hypodermic-like beak, and then siphons out her meal of blood—for without blood she could not live.   She uses her saliva to lubricate the entry of her beak as she inserts it beneath the skin.   The stinging sensation and subsequent irritation caused by her bite is due not only to the mechanical injury to skin tissues by the entry of the beak, but also to the chemical reaction set up by the introduction of her saliva into the body.   A mosquito *bites* by means of her mouthparts; a bee *stings* by means of her modified ovipositor.

Why mosquitoes are attracted to some people more than to others is a question still unanswered by scientific research. Another unsolved point is why some people scarcely notice the bite of a mosquito while others actually become ill. However, there is some consolation in feeling the sharp bite of a mosquito for, according to some authorities, bites of mosquitoes long associated with the carrying of disease organisms are hardly felt.

At least thirteen diseases are transmitted by mosquitoes, the most widely known being malaria and yellow fever. Malaria has been considered the most important disease of man since ancient times and it has hampered agriculture, trade, exploration, and the administration of colonies in tropical and subtropical areas. It is not definitely known whether malaria was endemic on the American continent before the coming of the Spanish conquistadors or whether they introduced it here, but the Spanish colonists, noting the ravages of this disease in the lowlands of the New World, took precautions by building their larger cities such as Mexico City, La Paz in Bolivia, and Quito in Ecuador, at higher altitudes. It is true that lowlands are more likely to be affected, but it is not necessarily true that malaria cannot occur at higher altitudes since it has occurred in Quito, at an elevation of nine thousand feet.

Although not known by the name of malaria, the symptoms have been recognized as those of a disease since the time of Hippocrates. It was named "malaria" in the middle of the eighteenth century in the belief that the disease was air-borne from the bad air (*mal aria*) rising from swamps and marshes. It was not until 1898 that Sir Ronald Ross, M.D., discovered that malaria or ague was caused by the bite of a malaria-infected mosquito. There are several species of mosquitoes that are capable of transmitting malaria but they are usually confined to the tropics or subtropics for they must have moisture and warmth in order to thrive.

As a rule malaria kills slowly after years of intermittent attacks of ague and fever which maim its victim physically and mentally. It is exceedingly debilitating and saps physical reserve to the point where one may become easy prey to some minor infection or disease which in itself would not ordinarily be fatal.

Yellow fever or "yellow jack" is also a mosquito-transmitted disease. When adult the yellow-fever mosquito is strikingly marked on the thorax and terminal segments of the legs with silvery white or yellowish stripes which alternate with black areas.   This striped appearance is so marked that the yellow-fever mosquito has become known as the "Tiger" mosquito.   It has a wide distribution where the temperature is hot and humid (it cannot thrive in a dry climate) and its range is usually confined in and about human habitations.

Yellow fever played an important part in our acquisition of the Panama Canal. About the turn of the century the French were attempting to force the completion of the canal but yellow fever frustrated their attempts.   Men died so fast that fabulous wages were offered as an inducement to get men to go to Panama and work on the project, some high French officials being paid as much as $50,000 to $100,000 a year.   They lived high while they resigned themselves to imminent death, as is attested by the English guardsmen's drinking song which they adopted:

> "Stand! Stand to your glasses steady,
>   'Tis all we have left to prize,
> One cup to the dead already,
>   Hurrah, for the next that dies."

After the French had spent about $260,000,000 and sacrificed over 2,000 French lives and the lives of 20,000 other workers to yellow fever they gave up the job and turned it over to the United States.   In 1904 the Americans paid Panama the preliminary $10,000,000 called for in the treaty and took over the completion of the canal.   Surgeon General W. C. Gorgas, U.S.A., took charge and his sanitation corps immediately went to work removing suspected victims of the disease to isolation hospitals, fumigating homes, pursuing and slaying all mosquitoes detected, and deluging breeding places with larvae-killing insecticides.   So thoroughly carried out was this mosquito campaign that within one year yellow fever was completely eradicated from the Isthmus.

Yellow fever also was the terror of the Caribbean sailors and West

African traders. The deadly jaundice from which it got the name *yellow* fever, was the origin of the yellow color adopted and still used for the quarantine flag.

It is interesting to note that in Bolivia, families who store their drinking water in huge earthenware containers are required by law to keep tiny fish in the water to eat up mosquito larvae in order to reduce the incidence of yellow fever. If they neglect to put fish in their store of drinking water official inspectors pour oil into the jars as a means of compelling the owners to clean them out.

There are many interesting stories about mosquitoes. According to an Algonquin Indian tale, mosquitoes were sent by Wakonda, the Strong Spirit (one of the Great Spirits), because of the laziness of a woman. They tell the legend in this way. Long ago an industrious Indian named Pug-a-mah-kon often had to work in dirty places. His wife, instead of keeping his deerskin clothes clean, neglected such duties and spent her time gossiping with her neighbors. When Pug-a-mah-kon heard that Wakonda was about to pay a visit to the village, he entreated his wife to clean his clothes for this momentous occasion. She failed to do so, and full of disgust at her failure to comply with his wishes, he was in the midst of chiding her for her indolence, when Wakonda suddenly appeared before them. Wakonda commanded Pug-a-mah-kon to take some of the dirt still clinging to the garment and to throw it at his wife. As the particles of dirt touched her they at once changed into mosquitoes. Ever since, especially during the warm days and nights of early summer, when mosquitoes are bothersome with their singing and biting, the Indians say it is a reminder of this lazy, slovenly woman, who was not only a trial to her husband, but who, because of her lack of industry, brought such a scourge upon all people.

The Creek Indians, on the other hand, perform a "mosquito dance" in which the women are supposed to play jokes on the male dancers by pricking them with pins.

Among the Ainu tribe, a primitive and exceptionally hairy people living in the northern end of Japan, we find another version of the origin of mosquitoes. Once upon a time there lived a great hobgoblin in the middle of the mountain range in Ainu-land. He was very large and his body was covered with so much hair that his skin looked like that of a bear. Possessed of only one eye in the middle of his forehead, he was indeed a fearsome-looking creature who was known to feed upon any human being that came within his reach. One day a brave young hunter in search of game unknowingly went near the hobgoblin's haunt. When he suddenly realized the nearness of the hobgoblin, instead of fleeing in terror, he took careful aim with his arrow and succeeded in hitting the creature in the center of its single eye. The hobgoblin immediately tumbled over dead for the eye was his vital spot. To make sure that so foul a thing was really dead, the hunter burned its body. Then he scattered the ashes in the wind. But lo! The ashes became gnats, mosquitoes, and gadflies [horse-flies]. However, concludes the myth, we must not grumble at these, for the lesser evil of flies is not as bad as the greater evil of having the one-eyed, man-eating monster among us.

In his "History of the Six Nations" David Cusick tells the story of the Great Mosquito: About the time when an Indian tribe was firmly settled in Fort Onondaga, a great mosquito invaded the place. It was a mosquito that was very mischievous to the people. Flying about the Fort, and equipped with a long stinger, this huge mosquito sucked the blood of numerous men, women, and children. The warriors made several attempts to expel the monster but each time met with failure, and they continued to be beset. One day, when The Holder of the Heavens paid their chief a visit, the mosquito made his appearance. The Holder of the Heavens immediately attacked the monster. After a few days' chase the monster's energy began to fail and it was finally overcome and killed near the salt lake Onondaga—but, before the monster died, each drop of the enormous quantity of blood it shed turned into a small mosquito!

From our eastern coast comes our best preventative (?) for the bites of these mosquitoes. Of course we all know that when a mosquito settles on a person, that person instinctively gets ready to swat it. But from this area we learn that there is a better way, providing one has the required self-control, and that is to hold one's breath as soon as the mosquito settles. This is supposed to clamp the mosquito's "bill" in the flesh, making it possible for the intended victim to reach out leisurely, capture it, and then destroy it quickly, or torture it slowly—depending on just how angry he feels toward mosquitoes at that moment!

MAGGOTS

The beneficial effect of the maggots (larvae) of the common blowfly in the healing of open wounds was accidentally discovered on the battlefields of the Civil War. Soldiers wounded in battle were, of course, brought into field hospitals as quickly as possible, but after major engagements when casualties were great, many soldiers could not be brought in for days, especially those wounded in outlying areas. When medical men finally got to these badly wounded soldiers they thought them to be beyond effective medical help because the wounds were filled with crawling maggots. This occurred during the summer months—the breeding season of flies—for flies usually die at the approach of cold weather. Contrary to expectations that these men would not live, or that they would surely be amputation cases, they not only recovered more rapidly but there were fewer amputations among them than among soldiers who had been brought into the hospitals and treated almost at once.

Several years passed before the maggots were cultured and found to be the larvae of blowflies. Experiments followed and maggots bred under laboratory conditions were placed in wounds that would not heal. It was then that the healing secret was found—it rested in the habits of these particular flies. The adult females were attracted to decaying flesh, wherein they laid their eggs, and wherein the eggs hatched into maggots in a matter of several hours. They immediately started crawling and feeding on dead tissue and decaying flesh, avoiding and doing no damage to healthy tissue, and as part of their feeding process they excreted substances which aided healing.

The use of maggots in the treatment of a serious bone infection (osteomyelitis) was introduced in medical circles only about thirty years ago. This was known as maggot therapy and sterile maggots that had been grown under laboratory conditions were employed. Within the last few years maggot therapy has been discontinued in favor of chemical treatment, since analysis proved that the healing was due to the substances which these maggots exuded, of which urea was the most important. These substances have now been synthesized and the chemical is manufactured at low cost. The use of chemicals has also served to overcome the unfavorable psychological reactions that took place when live maggots were employed.

There is a common expression that a person is "maggoty," or that a person "has maggots in his head," meaning, of course, that he is mentally unbalanced. It is probable that this expression arose from seeing the freakish activities of sheep infested by botflies. However, there is good reason for freakish activity on the part of sheep so infested because the animal is very often so blinded by pain that it goes dashing recklessly over the pastures, literally wearing itself out. The flies capable of causing this kind of injury are the botflies which are also known as breeze flies, warble flies, or gadflies. The females, while in flight, usually deposit living young, one at a time, on the nose of the sheep by brushing against it. These larvae then work up the nasal passages and eventually penetrate the nasal and frontal sinuses. Heavy infestations may actually result in the death of the sheep. These maggots, which feed upon the mucus and destroy the membranes, may attain a length of over an inch before they leave the animal by dropping to the ground for their pupation—where they sometimes pass two months before emerging as adult sheep botflies. The larvae, or maggots, of "bots" found in the head of sheep and goats, were once prescribed as a remedy for leprosy. Whether or not the cure was effective is not recorded, but the story does show that the ancients were aware of the fact that maggots made their way into the cranial cavity of animals.

There is a species of botfly, probably *Hypoderma lineata*, which deposits its eggs on the backs of caribou, usually along the spine anywhere from the neck to the tail, and when the eggs are deposited in great numbers this deposition will extend downward along the sides of the animal. Sometimes a number of botflies may deposit several hundred eggs on one animal. Such an occurrence would be considered a heavy infestation. When the eggs hatch into larvae, the larvae burrow through the caribou's skin to the tissues beneath, and there they feed and grow. By the time they have come to the end of the feeding period, which would be their last larval stage, they are quite large. Then they must emerge, drop to the ground and therein complete their development, to eventually come out of the ground as adult botflies in the same manner as do sheep botflies. Their emergence from the caribou's back is accomplished by boring their way upward and outward, leaving the skin so riddled with holes that it is entirely useless as a hide. While caribou will survive normal and even fairly heavy invasions of these botfly parasites, an exceptionally heavy infestation will kill them.

From the Hudson Bay region in the eastern part of Canada up through the northwestern part of North America, the Indians use caribou very much as we do horses. During the summer season these domesticated caribou become infested with bots. When the infesting insects reach the last larval stage, huge boil-like swellings indicate the precise sites where the maggots are about ready to emerge. At such times the Dogrib Indians of the Athapascan tribe that live between the Great Bear and the Great Slave Lakes will eat the maggots. They force the maggots out by applying pressure to the swellings and then eat them while still alive. If a caribou is slaughtered for food at a time when it is heavily infested with maggots, these Indians do not bother to remove them but simply cook the meat and enjoy it as it is—maggots and all.

Warm-blooded animals, both domestic—commonly, cows and horses—and wild—rabbits, foxes, deer, raccoons—may be infested in a like manner by bots. Such infestations are usually indicated by bumps or swellings similar to those described earlier. When the swellings reach large proportions the maggots can be removed by being squeezed out, in the manner employed by the Dogrib Indians. Bot infestations in our domestic farm animals are not too prevalent today because of the wide use of insecticides. But it has been recorded that in Kentucky a "faith-doctor" had the power to cure "bots" in cattle or horses by rubbing the animal with his hand nine times from the tip of the nose to the end of the tail, while repeating certain mysterious words known only to himself, and ending by slapping the animal on the side. It was believed that if a faith-doctor attempted to teach another man this "rite" he would lose his power, but that he could repeat the words to a woman without this danger. How the line of faith-doctors was perpetuated, if they still exist, is not recorded.

There are certain other fly maggots which infest the heads of maize (Indian corn). To get rid of the maggots a curious practice is observed among the head-hunters of the Amazon River. A heavily infested maize head is picked and around it is wrapped tobacco leaves which are chewed and mixed with capsicum (known in commerce as Tabasco pepper). Then the entire mass is wrapped in more leaves and the bundle is taken into the house where it is left until it is dry and half consumed by the maggots. When it has reached this state it is thrown away and by this performance it is believed that the maggots will disappear from the corn plantation.

The larva of the fly commonly known as the drone fly (*Eristalis tenax*), feeds upon decaying matter in shallow pools of water. The tubelike, telescoping tail of this larva reaches to the surface and carries air to the insect below the surface of the water. Réaumur, a great naturalist of the eighteenth century, studied this curious larva and found its vitality so extraordinary that he applied the scientific name of *tenax*, meaning "tenacious," to it. He also gave the larva its common name, "the rat-tailed maggot," by which it has been known ever since.

FLIES (other than mosquitoes)

In its adult stage the drone fly so closely resembles a bee in size, shape and color, that it has helped to create one of the most persistent myths—the widespread belief in the "ox-born bee." Such flies are often seen about the carcasses of animals, in the fluid of which they deposit their eggs, but the ancients, mistakingly believing that such flies were bees, concluded that bees were produced in the decaying carcasses of larger animals. The belief in the "ox-born bee" grew, and there was much discussion also concerning the animals from which certain other insects came. Some contended that while bees came from an ox exclusively, wasps originated from asses, drones from horses, and hornets from mules. The ancients also were of the firm belief that the "king" (or what later become known as the "queen bee") was produced from the brain of the ox, and that the worker bees were produced from its flesh. Chinese and Japanese writings reveal that the idea of the "ox-born bee" was current in the Orient at a very early date. Greek writers referred to the "ox-born bee" in their epigrams, and Archelos called them "the streaming children of the decaying ox," but even before the rise of Greece the Egyptians along the mouth of the Nile prescribed a laborious ritual in an attempt to produce bees from oxen. They buried a slain ox in the ground, with only the horns sticking out, and then sawed off the horns. From these openings, as the carcass decayed, bees were supposed to fly. Egypt, under the Ptolemies, seems to have been the center of this belief. One of the reasons why such attempts to produce bees continued was that for centuries seasonal inundation of the Nile Valley destroyed beehives so that whole colonies of bees died from famine and disease. Virgil (Georgics iv, verses 281–559) recorded the myth that was the basis for the belief: Aristaeus, the demigod, benefactor of mankind, who taught men to hunt and to keep bees, lost his hives by famine and disease. In his distress he appealed to his mother, and through her intervention, and that of the sea-god Proteus, he was initiated into the mystic rite by which a swarm of bees was produced from a slaughtered ox.

The belief that bees were developed from the decaying carcasses of animals persisted until comparatively recent times, but, of course, the simplest kind of an experiment—the attempt to obtain honey—would at any time have proven that these insects were not bees. What the ancients described, produced *flies* aplenty, among them *Eristalis tenax*, the fly that *looks* like a bee, but naturally, not a single *bee*.

Pliny mentions that during a festival in honor of Apollo an ox was sacrificed to flies and a god of flies was invoked for relief from the flies' annoying visits. Baal was called the Lord of Flies and was thought to defend the people from them, especially at places of sacrifice where flies were attracted in great numbers. The idol of Baal usually was represented by the figure of a fly, and thus to the ancients the fly became an object of adoration.

Why flies are scavengers is explained by our North American Indians in the following myth: Once two tribes of little people lived near each other. The difference between them lay in the fact that one tribe looked for food and put it safely away for the winter, while the other tribe played and sang and danced all day. The first winter the busy workers were sorry for their friends and fed them from their stored supplies. Thus the tribe that had by no means earned it was as comfortably fed as if they too had worked diligently all summer. The following summer the lazy tribe again wasted their time in playing and singing and dancing. That fall the workers moved away and left the lazy tribe to starve. The lazy tribe wailed and bemoaned their fate, whereupon the Great Spirit decided to teach them a lesson. He first gave the workers wings and made them bees, and then to the lazy tribe said: "You shall be flies and also have wings, but while the workers fly from flower to flower and eat the yellow honey, your food shall be that which has been thrown away!"

The Mission Indians of California have a legend which accounts for the fly's peculiar habit of rubbing its feet together. Tee-chai-pai (The Maker) was greatly concerned with his people's steadily dwindling supply of food and drink. He appeared before them and gave them one of three choices: To die and have done with life forever; to live forever; to die for a time and then return. They debated the merits and disadvantages of each choice but though they talked for days they seemed unable to make up their minds. It was at this point that the fly came along and said: "Oh you men, why do you talk so much? Tell him you want to die and have done with life forever!" Thus influenced, his people gave their choice to The Maker—to die and have done with life forever. That is why, ever since, the fly has rubbed his feet together in a supplicating gesture—begging forgiveness for those words he so testily uttered.

Many South American Indians say that spirits and demons sometimes assume the shape of insects. The Auraucanian Indians believe that departed tribesmen, chiefs in particular, take on the form of horseflies. These insects are regarded as spirits from the Beyond, which the Auraucanians call "Shadeland," and horseflies appearing at their frequent "drinking bouts" are accepted as an indication that their dead kinsmen are taking part in the feast. When such insects enter a village where someone is sick the Indians begin to wail as if death had already occurred, and say: "The souls of his dead relatives have come to fetch him away."

Another species of horsefly, and one that has been immortalized in song, is "The Blue Tail Fly" (*Tabanus atratus*). This is a fly that has a vicious bite and that ranges east of the Mississippi from Florida all the way up to Canada. While "The Blue Tail Fly" is an old folk song, it was revived in the late 1940's and became so popular that it rose to number one on the radio's "Hit Parade" of songs. The verses are as follows:

> When I was young I us'd to wait
> On Massa and hand him de plate;
> Pass down de bottle when he git dry,
> And brush away the blue tail fly.

> Chorus: Jimmy crack corn an' I don't care
>   Jimmy crack corn an' I don't care
>   Jimmy crack corn an' I don't care
>   Ole Massa gone away.

> An when he ride in the arternoon
> I follow wid a hickory broom;
> De poney being berry shy,
> When bitten by the blue tail fly.

> Chorus

> One day he rode aroun' de farm,
> De flies so numerous dey did swarm;
> One chance' to bit 'im on the thigh,
> De debble take dat blue tail fly.

> Chorus

> De poney run, he jump an' pitch,
> An' tumble Massa in de ditch;
> He died, an' de jury wonder'd why
> De verdic' was de blue tail fly.

> Chorus

Dey laid 'im under a 'simmon tree,
His epitaph am dar to see;
Beneath di stone I'm forced to lie,
All by de means ob de blue tail fly.

Chorus

In a great many communities insects serve as barometers and often, throughout the United States, one will hear it said that when flies are exceedingly numerous and bad (when they bite), it is a sign of rain. What the lay person does not realize is that these "biting" flies, which so closely resemble houseflies, are really stableflies. Stableflies are vicious biters and if given the opportunity will suck blood for from two to five minutes at a time, or until their abdomens are so swollen with blood that they bulge. These flies breed in decaying vegetation and manure. When they become numerous it is really an indication that there is a favorable breeding place somewhere in the vicinity—regardless of whether or not rain is on the way.

There are many other superstitions about flies. For example, in Massachusetts, dreaming of flies supposedly foretells sickness. It is also supposed to foretell sickness if a great many flies come into the house. In Louisiana and Kentucky, if a fly buzzes around a person continually, it is considered a sign that someone wants to see that person. Killing the fly is supposed to assure a meeting. In Scotland, among the deep sea fishermen, it is considered a sure omen of good luck if a fly falls into the glass just as a person is about to drink.

Sometime previous to the publication of his book in 1743, Big John Brickell, a doctor of medicine and a naturalist, came from England to settle in North Carolina to study the flora and fauna in the New World. While conducting his studies he associated with and obtained most of his information from Indian tribes. He records the practice of using large "mackerel flies" as an essential ingredient for curing baldness. He said: "The powders of these insects and their juice cure baldness." However, in none of the literature can a reference be found concerning a fly by the name of "mackerel fly." Because of Dr. Brickell's association with Indians in that particular locale, it is more than likely that it was an extremely localized name for a group better known as snipe flies. These snipe flies are common in woods, especially near moist places, and may be found on foliage, on long grasses, and on tree trunks.

The females of a particular genus of snipe flies (*Atherix*) exhibit the unusual habit of congregating in great masses at the time of egg-laying. A female clings on a branch (usually a willow) overhanging a stream, and drops her eggs into the water below, where they complete their development. After depositing her eggs she will not fly away but remains clinging to the branch, and as other females arrive they in turn cling to her and deposit their eggs in the same formation. Thus, great clusters of flies, several inches deep, are formed. This clustering for deposition of eggs is their last activity. They will never move again and even after death they are found still clinging together in great masses.

When such groupings took place the Modoc Indians of the Pitt River in California gathered them by the following method. They would place logs across the river and then go upstream to shake the congregated flies off the bushes. The flies fell on the water, floated downstream and lodged against the logs in great quantities. As many as a hundred bushels a day could be secured in this way. The Indians used a basket to dip the flies from the water and to carry them to their ovens, where they were cooked. They were not taken out of the oven immediately, but were allowed to cool gradually. The Indians called this dish "Koo-chab-bie." When cold, it was about the consistency of headcheese and was then ready to eat. It had a reddish-brown color and was firm enough to be cut into slices with a knife.

MISCELLANEOUS

PROVERBS:

"Even a lion must defend himself against the flies."
"Take not a musket to kill a fly."
" 'Almost' never killed a fly."
"Big flies break the spider web."
"Every fly has its shadow."
"A fly even has its own anger."
"A fly is busiest about lean horses."
"Flies are easier caught with honey than vinegar."

"Flies don't light on a boiling pot."

"Make yourself honey and the flies will devour you."

"Hungry flies bite sore."

"Where there is honey, there will the flies swarm."

"No fly gets into a shut mouth."

"Cover yourself with honey and the flies will have at you."

"One fly does not provide for another."

"A drop of honey catches more flies than a hogshead of vinegar."

"The fly that bites the tortoise breaks its beak."

"The fly that sips treacle is lost in the sweets."

"A fly before his own eyes is bigger than an elephant in the next field."

"If the fly flies, the frog goes not supperless to bed."

"Some people 'strain at a gnat and swallow a camel.' "

GENERAL:

When the gnats swarm, rain and warmer weather are believed to be coming. (Kentucky).

SYMBOL:

Mexico has used the mosquito on a revenue stamp for the purpose of collecting funds to combat malaria.

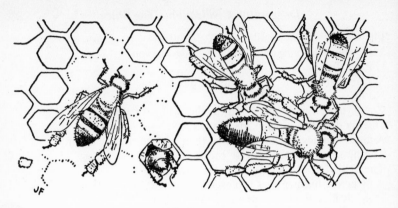

Chapter VI

Industrious Workers

The Bees

For hundreds of years bees, ants, and wasps have been the favorites of students studying animal behavior. The behavior of these insects has been the subject of numerous volumes by many famous naturalists. On the subject of bees alone, over two thousand books and bulletins have been written concerning their habits and methods of handling them in domestication. However, much still remains to be learned concerning even our most common species.

This Order, Hymenoptera, is very large, and *in addition* to the better known members such as the bees, the ants, and the wasps, it includes numerous less familiar forms. The lesser known forms include a far greater number of species than the better known types, and generally, also live solitary rather than group lives. Here we will be concerned primarily with the insects that live in colonies, or "the socializers" as they have been popularly captioned. It should be emphasized, however, that among the less familiar forms are many species of insect parasites which are of great economic importance. According to the species involved, they attack caterpillars of moths and butterflies, or mag-

84

gots of flies, or grubs of beetles, or nymphs of bugs, and some species attack aphids. They vary greatly in size ranging from the quite large, measuring a few inches in length, to the smallest insects so far known in the animal kingdom—species of minute egg-parasites which measure but a mere twenty-one one-hundredths of a millimeter. These little known forms are responsible for the fact that millions of insect pests never live to lay eggs for another brood.

In entomological literature one finds the explanation that insects in this order have been named Hymenoptera because of the membranous nature of their four wings. However, this is not *the* distinctive character because their wings are similar to those of several other groups of insects. Another meaning has been put forth by a research entomologist, Robert K. Nabour, who thinks it more logical that they have been so named because of the predominantly conspicuous and specialized marriage flight. Nabour believes that, translated, Hymenoptera means: *Hymen* = marriage; *ptera* = on-the-wing—or "marriage while flying."

The mouthparts of the insects classified as Hymenoptera vary. Some are adapted for chewing, others for lapping or sucking liquid food, and in still others the mouthparts are adapted to perform both functions.

The larvae are caterpillarlike in form and some are similar to the larvae of flies, being maggotlike with no legs.

It is among this group of insects that we find a number of unusual methods of reproduction. In several forms of minute parasitic wasps the number of young produced is not dependent upon the number of eggs laid, because among these insects many embryos are developed from a single egg. It has been established that in this style of reproduction (termed polyembryony) an average of 163 adult parasites developed from a single egg. Parthenogenesis—the production of young by females that have not mated—is also known to occur among Hymenoptera. Sometimes a queen honeybee produces eggs before she has mated; from such eggs only males are developed. In some recorded instances, worker bees and worker ants, neither of which mate, also produce eggs which develop only into males.

In evolving their social system, the community-building bees, ants, and wasps, have developed highly specialized females called queens. The queen honeybee, which is believed to mate but once in a lifetime, has developed a tiny internal pouch in which the male germ cells are stored. As the queen lays her eggs she is able to open or close this pouch and thus control whether each egg shall or shall not be fertilized. The ones that are fertilized develop into females, and those that are not develop into males. In this way, it might be said that the honeybee queen exercises the power of controlling sex.

Bees exhibit great differences in habits. The stingless bees of the tropics, the domesticated honeybees, and the bumblebees are social— living together cooperatively in colonies consisting of many individuals. Some species are solitary—each female providing a nest for her own young; others are parasitic—the females laying their eggs in the nests of other species of bees.

A number of solitary bees (for example, the *Apathus* mentioned in the poem which follows) construct no nests of their own but live as "inquilines" or "cuckoo parasites" in nests of other species of bees. In this case, the female *Apathus* hunts up a *Bombus* colony (bumblebee nest) and lays her eggs in it while the *Bombus* is out searching for food for her own offspring. When the female *Bombus* returns, she never becomes aware of the fact that there are strange eggs among her own.

At the February, 1889 meeting of the Entomological Society of Washington, there occurred an animated discussion on the habits of *Bombus* and *Apathus*. The majority of the members held the view that *Apathus* is an inquiline. One of the members whose name was not recorded thereupon wrote the following verses:

> Oh! an Apathus sat on a Chrysanthemum
> A-cleaning her antennae,
> And she little thought of the Pyrethrum
> That would take her life away!

> And there she sat, a-taking a rest,
> And smiled in a satisfied way,
> For she'd laid ten eggs in a Bombus nest
> And there'd soon be the de'il to pay.

For her offspring dear, her very first brood,
    Would hatch in a very short time,
And no trouble she'd have a storing up food,
    For she worked on the Cuckoo line.

Her young would hatch 'ere the young bumblebees,
    And the young bumblebees would die,
While the young Apathi would live at their ease
    And fatten like pigs in a sty!

So she sat in the sun, this wicked old bee,
    And scratched her tibiae,
And chuckled inside in a lazy glee
    At the business she'd done that day.

But the Chrysanthemum on which she sat
    Belonged to a neat old maid,
Whose plants were her pride (next to her cat),
    And that day she was out on a raid

Against Aphids and slugs, with a Buhach-gun
    Filled with Peter's and Milco's best,
And seeing the Apathus, just for fun,
    She dusted her yellow vest.

Lord! how the cheat kicked as she fell to the ground!
    And how she did buzz and hum!
But she never got well—she never "came round"—
    Her fraudulent life was done.

From this little tale can a moral be drawn—
    How the bumblebee loafs not a bit;
But works all day from the earliest dawn,
    And thus 'scaped the death-dealing hit?

This moral is good, but please don't forget
    Those eggs that the Apathus hid!
The Bombus is working and slaving yet,
    But it's all for the other one's kid!

STINGS

Among the bees, wasps, and hornets, the capacity for stinging is used both for purposes of defense against enemies and offense, in order to procure food for the young.   Their secretions have irritating properties to which the "sting" is due.   Like the mosquito, the female of the species "is more deadly than the male" since it is the female which is provided with a specialized ovipositor that is efficiently developed for the piercing of other insects, or for the piercing of the skin of higher animals.   The organ known as the ovipositor is a dual purpose, tube-like structure.   The queens use it as a means of laying their eggs, while the workers, which are incapable of laying eggs, use it solely for stinging purposes.   This ovipositor and/or stinging apparatus is situated on the last abdominal segment of the bees, the wasps, and the hornets.

FIGURE 18.   The Sting of a Honeybee Left: Location of ovipositor or sting at tip of abdomen.
Right: Greatly enlarged drawing to show the barbs on the two alternate shafts that comprise the ovipositor or sting.

The saying that a honeybee can sting only once is true.   The reason for this is to be found in the structure of her stinging apparatus which is made up of two spears having several fishhook-like barbs on each spear.   When the honeybee strikes, the longest spear penetrates the flesh, quickly followed by the alternate penetration of the other spear.   Once her sting is imbedded in the flesh of her enemy the honeybee pays with her life, since in attempting to withdraw it she pulls off that vital part of her abdomen to which the sting is attached.   The poison (a secretion supplied by two glands, one acid and the other alkaline) is forced to the ends of the spears by muscular contraction, in much the same way that venom is forced through the fangs of a snake.   The bumblebees, the wasps, and the hornets do not have fishhook-like barbs on their stinging probes and for that reason can sting repeatedly without injury to themselves.

According to the Algonquin Indians, the bees, wasps, and hornets did not always have the ability to sting, and they tell the following story of how these insects acquired this means of protecting themselves. Ages ago, the bees were just as industrious as they are now, but they experienced trouble in keeping their honey from being stolen by their numerous enemies. In vain they hid their honey stores in the hollows of trees and in the clefts of rocks. Bears, squirrels, and birds with long beaks often stole their honey, and this resulted in entire swarms of bees starving during the long winters. They tried scattering into small groups and storing just enough honey to keep themselves fed from season to season, but even this failed, and finally they became desperate. They then appealed for help to Wakonda. He listened to their tale of woe and was for a time uncertain as to the best method of aiding them. Meanwhile, he dismissed them, asking them to come back upon a certain date. They were so overjoyed at the prospect of relief that instead of keeping it secret, they told their cousins, the hornets and the wasps. When the appointed time to visit Wakonda came the bees were on hand, and along with them had come their cousins. After praising the bees for their industry, Wakonda proceeded to give them the terrible barbed stings which they have had ever since. And then, since the wasps and the hornets claimed to be their cousins, the Great Spirit good-naturedly endowed them too with stinging weapons.

Tolerance to bee stings appears to be developed in the case of beekeepers, but this tolerance is lost in time when they are no longer exposed to bee stings. One scientist has estimated, after much laboratory experimentation, that five hundred honeybee stings is a lethal dose for a man. And yet, there is a case on record in Irvington, New York, in which a young man died within fifteen minutes after one sting on the back of his neck. The attending physician said the victim was unusually sensitive to bee venom and recalled that when the same man had been stung in the leg two years previously it had required twelve hours of artificial respiration in addition to injections of adrenalin to revive him. There is increasing evidence that the severe reaction of some persons to bee stings is due to protein hypersensitivity and not necessarily to the bee venom itself.

Centuries ago, Hippocrates, Galen, and Celius wrote about the remedial value of the stings of the honeybees, and ancient beekeepers actually gave treatments right at the hive! Pliny wrote that even bears "come from winter sleep, dull and torpid, and rob hives not for honey alone. Their eyesight is dull and for which reason they seek combs of bees, that from stinging, oppression in the head may be relieved."

There is widespread belief today that persons habitually exposed to honeybee stings do not suffer from rheumatism, and many persons afflicted with rheumatic disorders often allow themselves to be stung by honeybees, hoping for relief. Chemical analysis has recently revealed that honeybee venom contains a substance that acts favorably to minimize rheumatic pain.

In recent years honeybee venom therapy, by means of injection, has become standardized clinical procedure in the treatment of rheumatic conditions. By injection of a standardized dose, greater control can be exercised than is possible by allowing a living bee to sting as it is held in contact with the flesh. Honeybee venom is now put up in ampules, each ampule containing the equivalent of from one to ten stings. It looks like water and is said to taste like bananas. In laboratories, girls using tweezers remove stings from gassed bees at the rate of 1000 to 1500 an hour. The stings and their attached venom sacs are ground and pounded fine in mortar and pestle machines. It is also made into salve, which, when applied to the surface of the skin, penetrates readily. Some trade names for bee preparations are Apis Mellifica, Apicosan, Ven-Apis, Apisin, Immenin, Emmenim, Lyovac, Forapin, and Apis Viris.

Of passing interest is a dispatch from Paris (June 29, 1932) which reported that the curative effects of treating cancer with the venom of bees was being studied by the French Academy of Medicine. Members of the Academy were informed that by injecting the venom of honeybees into rabbits suffering from cancer, an inflammation was caused which retarded the growth of cancerous cells.

That bees were used as instruments of warfare and protection is brought out in a number of historical references. It is related that when a group of soldiers were about to plunder the property of the Roman poet Virgil, the attempt was successfully thwarted when his servants placed his most valuable possessions in beehives.

In olden days it was considered quite the thing to throw hives of bees down from besieged walls in order to rout the enemy below, and as recently as World War I the German soldiers in East Africa tossed beehives into the British ranks.   In 1937 this ancient custom was revived when strikers threw two hives of bees at policemen guarding a mill.   After vainly battling the insects for some time the police were rescued by the fire department which finally routed the bees with streams of water.

In western Pennsylvania it is said that bees will invariably sting redheaded persons as soon as they approach the hive.   It is claimed, however, that bees never sting idiots since the bees are "too discerning and generous," nor will they sting people who have good dispositions.

HONEYBEES

For a long time honeybees were known to our Indians by the name of "English flies" and the Indians considered them as a harbinger of the white man.   They said that in proportion as the honeybees advanced, the Indian and the buffalo retired.   Honeybees were not known to the Indians prior to the arrival of white men in this country; domesticated honeybees (*Apis mellifica*) were introduced in Boston by the English.   The bees gradually spread southward and in the year 1670 were carried over the Allegheny Mountains by a hurricane.   It is be-believed that no true honeybees existed on this hemisphere before there were European settlers, and that the beekeeping industry was not introduced until the coming of the Spanish conquerors.   In South America the history of the honeybee does not seem to begin until the nineteenth century.   Prior to the introduction of honeybees upon this continent the Aztecs used wild stingless bees as a source of honey and wax.

There is a widespread but mistaken belief, handed down for countless generations, that ringing a bell or beating pans while bees are swarming will drown out the order of the leader and cause the swarm to settle.   For centuries the leader was called the "King Bee," because ancient authors had noticed that in a hive there was always one noticeably larger and differently shaped bee; it was not until 1609 that the King Bee was determined to be a Queen Bee.

When honeybees swarm it means that a bee colony is dividing, with some of the bees remaining to maintain the old establishment and others going out to establish a new hive. The swarming from a single hive may not occur during an entire season, and then again it may take place many times. All of the reasons for the swarming of honeybees are not known, but the basic biological urge to perpetuate the species by establishing new colonies, and the need to relieve overcrowding, may very well be underlying factors. The swarm departing from a hive usually consists of the old queen and a large following of her workers and drones, and at such times they issue in a most peaceable mood and allow themselves to be handled. This may be partially explained by the fact that before leaving the old hive each worker swallows as much honey as she possibly can, which results in her obdomen being so distended that it is difficult for her to curve it—a necessary action preparatory to stinging.

Swarming usually takes place in the late spring and early summer when a new queen is bred within the hive. Queens attain royal status by dietary means alone, being fed "royal-jelly," a secretion produced by the nurse worker bees, during the larval stage. The larvae of the hive which are not fed this "royal-jelly" develop into smaller-sized bees—the workers—although *genetically* the queen and the worker bee are the same. Immediately preceding the emergence of the new queen, unrest pervades the hive. This causes some of the older drones and workers to rally around the old queen and leave the hive with her before the new queen emerges from her royal cell and stings to death all the other occupants of the "queen cells"—her potential young rivals in the hive. If the old queen has not left the hive by the time the new queen has emerged from her royal cell, it is because the old queen has aged to the point where she is no longer able to lay the number of eggs necessary to maintain the population of a hive, in which case she too is stung to death by the young queen. When this is done she has established her regal status. Then she begins her mid-air nuptial flight, and after she has mated she returns to her royal domain—the old hive—and starts laying eggs for the colony. In a thriving hive or colony, there are usually 75,000 bees, consisting of one queen, 400 to 500 drones, and the rest workers. The workers are the undeveloped females whose short lives (five to six weeks in the summer and five to six months in the winter) are entirely devoted to labor. The drones are the male honeybees.

There are many popular beliefs and superstitions concerning bees. To sell a beehive is supposed to bring bad luck: "If *one* hive is sold [for money] the contents of *two* hives will die." The sale of bees is generally accomplished by transferring them to another owner with the tacit understanding that a bushel of corn (the constant value of a swarm) is to be given in return. Other values of a hive of bees are contained in the following ditty:

> A swarm of bees in May
> Is worth a load of hay.
> A swarm of bees in June
> Is worth a silver spoon.
> A swarm of bees in July
> Is not worth a fly.

As a forecast of a severe winter in Maine it is believed that bees will lay up unusually large stores of honey, and almost every farmer believes that a bee can scent rain. They will solemnly quote:

> When bees to distance wing their flight,
> Days are warm and skies are bright.
> But when the flight ends near their home,
> Stormy weather is sure to come.

When death occurs in an Ozark family they often "tell the bees" by fastening bits of black cloth to each hive. These hillfolk believe that failure to do this is a slight to the bees which may result in desertion of the hive. They also believe that the beehives should be turned in the opposite direction in order to ward off other deaths in the family; that a hive of bees will not stay in the possession of a quarrelsome family; that it is not well for a person to eat honey from the hive of an enemy, and bad luck to use the wax of an enemy's bees.

From Louisiana we learn that a yellow honeybee flying around you foretells the receipt of good news; if a black one hovers over you "be prepared for bad news"; if a honeybee flies before you, you will get a letter, and if the bee is in the house it denotes pleasant company.

The southern Negro assigns many foretellings to the actions of bees in dreams. For instance, they believe that if bees are seen in a swarm it betokens death; if bees sting one it means betrayal; if one dreams of bees making honey it is a sign of honor, and to dream of killing a bee signifies great loss. Generally, it is a good omen to dream of bees.

POLLINATION

The honeybees differ from most other Hymenoptera in that they not only eat pollen and nectar themselves, but provision their nests with these substances for their young to eat. In the gathering of the nectar the bees perform a great service to man by transferring huge quantities of pollen from one flower to another, thus aiding in the fertilization of the blossoms. In 1946 the Department of Agriculture considered bees ten to twenty times more valuable as pollinators than as producers of honey and beeswax; one of the production goals they set was that the number of colonies of bees be increased by 8 per cent over 1945. The need for the production of honey and beeswax, although important, of course, was considered secondary to the need of bees as pollinating agents.

Periodic publicity is given to professional apiarists who transport hives of bees from orchard to orchard. The first such commercial introduction into apple orchards, for the purpose of pollination, occurred in 1926. That year, it is recorded, the apple harvest was increased by 40 per cent. Studies show that each rented hive (the average rental is $6 per hive) should have a minimum field force of 15,000 bees and that one hive is needed for each acre to be pollinated. Studies also show that each worker bee spends an average of seven and three-tenths seconds per apple blossom, and that within a period of a little over six minutes the bee will visit fifty blossoms. It has been estimated that bees pollinate 2,843,890 apple trees during one season and that in 1949 this resulted in a U.S. apple crop valued at ninety million dollars.

Many farmers now depend on rented bees to pollinate at least fifty

kinds of crops.   This has become necessary because of intensive cultivation and accompanying use of poisonous sprays which result in the
destruction of many natural pollinators.   Then, too, many natural
pollinators do not emerge early enough to pollinate the early blossoms.
Traveling has added greatly to the bees' productive capacity and a study
has shown that the average production of honey for each colony of stay-
at-home bees is 50 pounds per year, whereas those that travel produce,
on an average, 150 pounds per colony.   The hives are transported
by motor vehicles—648 colonies traveling comfortably and safely on
each truck.   One western company, located in Colton, California, has
26,000 colonies of bees which are "hired out" as agricultural workers
and follow seasonal crops.

To harvest Florida's famed white Tupelo honey in the remote sections of that State, particularly along the banks of the Apalachicola
River, many beekeepers use barges, transferring their beehives up and
down the river according to the season, in order to get the fine flavor
secreted by the gum tree blossoms.

Here again, this is not a new practice but merely a modern version
of an ancient custom; Pliny, in his "Natural History," mentioned it
nearly twenty centuries ago.   The inhabitants of the upper Nile River
region in Egypt traditionally placed their beehives on floats, in the
custody of professional boatmen, and the bees were thus supplied with
new pastures as the floats drifted from one village to another along
the Nile.   The hives were collected from different villages bordering
the river and arranged in orderly piles upon river boats.   The boats
were then floated down river and stopovers were made, of shorter or
longer duration, depending upon the produce of the surrounding country, the entire trip taking about three months.   For transporting their
hives the owners paid the boatmen in proportion to the number of hives
carried from one extremity of Egypt to the other.   This small invest-
ment paid good dividends, for when the hives were returned to their
owners they contained an abundance of wax and honey.   The honey,
having been culled mostly from orange and jasmine blossoms, was
always in great demand, because honey culled from these blossoms is
exceptionally delicious.

HONEY

History does not mention the first discovery of honey by human beings. Whether it became known to primitive man by accident, as a result of a bee-tree being split open by lightning, or by his observation of the fondness of animals for it, once man tasted the thick transparent liquid his fear of stings was overcome and he became a hunter of honey—nature's finished sweet product.

From Obermaier's *"Fossil Man in Spain."*
Courtesy of the Hispanic Society of America.

FIGURE 19. A rock painting at the Cuevas de la Araña, northwest of Bicorp, Valencia, Spain, representing a gatherer of wild honey in prehistoric times. The original painting is in red. The rock paintings in this cave (discovered in 1919) include marvelous paintings of various wild bees' nests in the holes in the rocks. This unknown ancient artist thus has left us a record of how our Stone Age ancestors robbed a bee's nest of its golden store. The drawings are of such antiquity that in a number of hunting scenes the animals portrayed are now extinct.

In the summer, each worker bee makes six to eight trips afield daily, to visit flowers from which she sucks the thin, watery liquid known as nectar, which she swallows and transports to the nest in her crop. While in the crop the nectar undergoes a chemical change and becomes modified into a heavy syrup containing numerous minerals and some vitamins. This is what we call honey. The bee's crop is a relatively large elastic, baglike organ, and it is here that the nectar is converted from sucrose (cane sugar) to levulose and dextrose (easily assimilated sugars). In the hive the bees regurgitate the honey into hexagonal waxen cells and then "cure" it by an elaborate system of fanning with their wings. The wax which the honeybees use to build their honeycombs is also a product of their digestion. The wax is secreted from a series of plates situated between the segments on the lower side of the honeybee's abdomen. After the honey is stored the bees seal the cells with wax, and then, when hungry, they uncap each cell, as needed, and lap up the honey. While the cells remain sealed the honey is preserved indefinitely.

The great variation in the color and quality of honey is entirely dependent upon the blossoms from which it has been gathered, and the flavor is due to the aromatic volatile oils in the flowers—the same oils that are responsible for the perfume of the flowers.

Careful investigation by the Iowa Agricultural Experiment Station has shown that it requires about 900 field bees to collect a single pound of raw nectar per day. But since a large part of this weight is lost in preparation, actually two to three times that amount is needed to make a pound of honey. The sugar concentration of the nectar also varies greatly among different types of blossoms—apple blossoms, for instance, having a greater concentration of sugar than pear blossoms. Therefore, even though great quantities of nectar may be brought to the hive, there is little left after the processing unless the sugar content is high.

Some early records of bees have been found among the ruins of ancient Egypt. In the year 1901 a German archaeologist, excavating in the region of Abusir, came upon a group of sculptures in low relief which told a complete story of Egyptian beekeeping. The bas-reliefs were found in the Temple of the Sun, estimated as being about 2600 B.C. They depict bee-raising in Egypt in an extremely advanced stage and show that in all probability it was already centuries old. The hives appeared quite like those which are still being used in the Nile Valley. According to present-day authorities this conclusion is substantiated by the finding of bees in Egyptian hieroglyphics dating back to 3500 B.C. In a royal Egyptian tomb, honey 3,000 years old was found, darkened and thickened by time, but still pure honey.

The honeybee has been the insect most used in the folklore, customs, symbolism, art, and religious rites of the peoples of history. This is undoubtedly because honey was man's only sweetening material for thousands of years. Honey cannot be tampered with without detection; if diluted with water it ferments, and if adulterated with corn syrup it separates out. There is nothing but pure honey on the market today since no one has yet found a way to synthesize, cheapen, or improve it.

Although the ancients did not have poisonous gas for use in warfare they used honey as a weapon which proved to be equally lethal. Heptakometes placed poisonous honey along Pompey's route while Pompey and three of his cohorts (about 1,000 men) were traveling through the mountains. Pompey's soldiers ate the honey, became senseless, and were set upon and killed. Scientists who have since visited these areas state that the bees fed on the nectar produced by an azalea known as *Rhododendron ponticum*. Honey produced from the nectar of these flowers is poisonous. At the present time it is carefully thrown away and only the beeswax is used.

During the Middle Ages honey played an important role in the art of healing. It was applied to ulcerated wounds as well as to fresh, bloody wounds. It was also recommended for inflammation of the mouth cavity and throat, as well as ulceration of the digestive tract. Honey, as a healing aid, is again gaining favor and is now used in the preparation of expectorants because of its remedial properties in ailments of the throat. Laboratory tests show that for wounds of the gums and tongue, honey is beneficial when taken into the mouth for a brief time and then swallowed slowly.

The American Bee Journal (1945) contained an interesting report concerning bees as "pharmacists." The Maikop (Russian) laboratories have experimented with feeding medicine to bees, using quinine, mixed in thin syrup. The drug neither spoils the bees' appetite for the syrup, nor does it affect them in any way. The result is a concentration of quinine in the honey which the bees produce. Quinine thus incorporated in honey is said to have medicinal values superior to the drug in any other form. The sulpha drugs have been used in the same way. Bees will also lap mint extract in syrup which results in honey with a pleasant flavor and a high vitamin C content.

Honey is used internally as well as externally in veterinary practice. A lean horse fed on honey and bran is said to put on flesh rapidly. Homer relates in the Iliad that Diomedes fed his horses honeyed barley.

In ancient China, honey was used as a medicine and as a component of special diets.   Even today, in the interior of China, honey can only be obtained in the old-style medicine shops.   For centuries the emblem of the doctor has been a snake coiled around the stick of Aesculapius, the mythological god of medicine who held the snake sacred.   The snake was the emblem of health and recovery, and supposedly was fed on honey or honeycakes.

Bread and honey were the chief foods of the ancient Pythagoreans and they attributed their freedom from disease to a daily portion of honey.   Confirmation of their faith in this belief is expressed by Dr. Bodag Felix Beck (1938) in his book "Honey and Health" when he explains that "honey has a distinct bactericidal power which is mainly due to its hygroscopic power.   All living organisms require a certain amount of moisture to maintain their lives.   When bacteria come in contact with honey they are deprived of the vital moisture and perish. The acid reaction of honey also renders it an unfavorable medium for the bacteria to grow in.   Most microscopic organisms which affect the human body are destroyed in honey."   Modern chemical analysts have established that honey, in addition to having a high vitamin content, contains potassium, sodium, calcium, magnesium, iron, copper, chlorine, phosphorus, manganese and sulphur, as well as enzymes that aid in the process of digestion.

The old mythologies praise the invigorating and health-giving qualities of honey and many references are made to its magic healing power. The Bible (both the Old and New Testaments), the Talmud, the Koran, the Sacred Books of India, Persia, and Egypt, all speak of honey, praising it as a food, a beverage, and a medicine.   The Hindus use honey to wash their household gods.

When Augustus Julius Caesar, dining with Pollio Rumilius on his one-hundredth birthday, inquired of him how he had preserved both vigor of body and mind, Pollio replied: "Interius melle, exterius olio." (Internally by honey, externally by oil.)   On festive occasions, or when celebrating a victory upon returning home from war, the Roman soldiers drank honey and wine (mulsum) to prolong their lives.   The Greek athletes ate honey before they entered the arena for the Olympic games and Homer described in the Iliad how these tired heroes also consumed honey while recuperating in Nestor's tent.

Honey is widely used as a food among primitive peoples. It is mixed with milk, curds, cheese, cereals, and bread, and in East Africa the natives not only eat the wild honey, but dilute it with water and let it ferment into a wine or beer (*tetsch*) which is their favorite drink.

Clear, sweet honey was the chief ingredient of the Divine Drink, sacred to the Druids. This "drink of the gods" was really fermented hydromel—honey wine—which was only later called meth or mead. Before the introduction of grape and malt liquors, mead was a universal drink. The ancient poetic name of Great Britain was the "Honey Isle of Beli," given because the islanders consumed great quantities of mead. Mead has remained the popular drink among primitive races. The African soothsayers and prophets, especially among the Hottentots, intoxicate themselves with honey wine and use it liberally during religious ceremonies and magical practices.

In France it is the custom for newlyweds to imbibe a honey drink daily for a period of thirty days following the marriage ceremony. As a result of this custom it is believed that the word honeymoon (honey-month) originated in France.

The educational process for an Orthodox Jewish boy begins at the age of five, when, in keeping with tradition, he kisses a drop of honey placed upon the first page he is to learn to read. Thus, at an impressionable age, he is taught to associate learning with sweetness. Centuries ago, he was also served honey cakes formed in the letters of the alphabet. When most of the world was illiterate a Jewish boy could read, and by the time he was thirteen he had advanced to the point where he was well versed in literature. In this way arose the love of learning and the keenness of intellect possessed by so many Jews. Interestingly enough, the theory that learning progresses more satisfactorily by means of pleasant associations is now accepted as an important aspect of educational philosophy.

In the Dekhan Brahman household, when a child is born, the first duty of a father is to drop honey into the mouth of the infant. These people also use it during courtship. When the bridegroom comes to the bride's house he is given honey and curds to sip. This is called *madhuparka* and its object is to scare evil away from the bridegroom.

For ages honey has also been used as a preserver of all organic matter.

In medieval England, meats and leather were cured in honey. In the Sudan, meat is boiled in honey as a means of preserving it. In Ceylon, honey instead of salt is used as a preservative. The preservation of organic matter with honey extends even to human remains. Alexander the Great was embalmed with honey, in combination with beeswax which is also a preservative. In Burma, when people die during the rainy season, the eviscerated corpses are preserved in honey until the relatives are able to procure dried firewood for the customary cremation. If the dead person is a Buddhist monk, when the corpse is removed from its receptacle for cremation the honey is put in one-ounce jars and sold at auction. The Burmese believe that a drop of this honey will cure any affliction.

The beneficial effect of honey on the skin also has an age-old repute. Poppea, the comely wife of Nero, was said to have used honey and asses' milk as a face lotion. The famous beauty, Madame DuBarry, used honey extensively in her toilet preparations, and the noted loveliness of the hands of Japanese women of noble birth is attributed to their daily use of fresh honey as a hand lotion. Even today many face creams and lotions contain honey since it is reputed to have a nourishing, bleaching, astringent, and antiseptic effect on the skin.

Honey is used in the preparation of all kinds of confections, jams, jellies, beverages, breads, cakes, candies, cookies, desserts, salad dressings, sandwich spreads, vegetables, and meats. In France honey is an ingredient of "Pain d'épice," a type of gingerbread which is sold in immense quantities at fairs. It keeps for a long period of time and the recipe may be of interest to some readers: Dissolve four ounces of soda in a glass of skimmed milk. Take four pounds of flour and pour in the milk and enough honey to make a thick dough. Flavor with anise and coriander seeds, cloves, cinnamon; all powdered fine. Knead carefully, as for bread. Let rise in a warm place two hours, spread in pans, and bake in moderately warm oven. Ten to twelve minutes will do if the cakes are thin. Wheat flour makes good "pain d'épice" but some prefer rye flour. Fall honey is preferred because of its stronger taste.

Eating the sweet produce of bees is accepted without much thought, but in the Yunnan Province of China the bees themselves are eaten. Fried bees (Fan-tse) have been sold for sixty cents a platter. In

Burma, the grubs, pupae, and eggs of honeybees are boiled together with parts of the comb and made into a kind of soup. In the case of an overloaded stomach some primitive tribes are well aware of the physiological benefit to be derived from the use of emetics, because at such times they eat the larvae of bees found in honeycombs to relieve their distress. And the Mincapies on the Andaman Islands are known to eat such larvae specifically to relieve constipation. Bee larvae have a laxative effect upon the human digestive system.

If you have heard about the "Honey War" and have wondered what it was all about, this was a dispute between the states of Iowa and Missouri. In 1840 a farmer of Clark County, Missouri, cut down several trees filled with honey. Because the trees grew on the boundary line between the two states, both states claimed the strip of land. In 1851, after eleven years of litigation, the United States Supreme Court finally settled the boundary, but by that time in legal circles the case had become known as "The Honey War."

BEESWAX

Another product of the honeybees which has always been in great demand is beeswax. When one considers that it takes about twenty pounds of honeycomb to make one pound of beeswax, the value of beeswax becomes apparent. The United States uses about ten million pounds of beeswax annually, six to seven million pounds being produced in this country and the balance imported; the Catholic Church alone uses approximately three million pounds annually. According to the traditional lore of Wales, a Catholic Mass cannot be celebrated without wax candles because bees draw their origin from Paradise, which they had to leave owing to man's transgression; but God gave them his blessing and bade them descend from heaven to earth where they could suck Divine Nectar out of every blossom, and produce light for the altar.

The need for wax is responsible for the following story telling us how honeybees were smuggled out of Egypt. Wax was needed as an offering after the New Covenant had been established, but in order to have wax it was necessary to have bees. People knew that a bee industry existed in Egypt but they also knew that they could not get permission to take bees out of that country. Saint Nicholas, celebrated in the Greek Church as the Wonder-Worker, was sent to smuggle some honeybees out of Egypt but he failed in the attempt. St. Sossima then volunteered to go and after he arrived in Egypt he managed to secure ten honeybees and a queen which he concealed in a hollow reed. The Egyptians, suspecting the purpose of his visit, searched him thoroughly but they did not find the bees because they never thought of investigating the reed. Supposedly, the honeybees which we now have are descendants of the honeybees that St. Sossima brought out of Egypt. In later years St. Sossima became the Christian patron saint of beekeeping in the Ukraine of Russia.

Beeswax has played a major part in the development of the arts. For centuries, sculptors have used it as a sculpturing material, and artists, even before the Christian era, developed a method of incrustic painting—the utilization of beeswax to incrust or overlay surfaces being decorated. Ancient goldsmiths in all parts of the world, without interchange of knowledge, used beeswax to perfect the "lost wax" process for the casting of metal objects, especially gold. This process derived its name from the fact that only one object could be cast, the wax being burned or "lost" in the process. This was the basis for the present-day dry metal-casting industry.

Far across the Pacific Ocean, where the colorful Dutch East Indian island of Java lies, the natives have for centuries been practicing their beautiful and imaginative art known as "Batik" or "wax painting." The techniques for the making of batik are numerous and differ from village to village, but it is beeswax that is basic to attaining the designs in the cloth.

Beeswax has been an important item in the process of making visual records of people. The ancient Egyptians made death masks with wax in memory of their dead; the wealthy citizens of ancient Rome posed for wax-sculptured portraits, and in the Middle Ages ecclesiastics used it to fashion images of saints. Prior to the introduction of plastics, beeswax was the ideal substance for the making of anatomical study figures in the field of science, and in certain cases it is still preferable. Originally the mannequins in shop windows were also made of beeswax.

Beeswax also has been the material used for the realistic portrayal of people who have achieved great fame. Among such portrayals are included royalty, statesmen, presidents, soldiers, religious leaders, as well as famous actors, actresses, and singers, and even criminals who have made world headlines. Exhibits of these figures are found in waxworks museums. Years ago there were a number of outstanding waxworks museums, notably one in France that went bankrupt at the beginning of the 19th century, and the Eden Musée in New York City that was destroyed by fire in 1915. However, the one founded by Madame Tussaud in London in 1833 still stands. It was swept by fire in 1925, but since the molds had been saved, many of the destroyed figures were recast and placed on exhibit again three years later. For over one hundred years Madame Tussaud's waxworks museum has remained a popular place of interest for tourists, and in recent years it has been attracting about one million visitors yearly. The lifelike figures on exhibit number about five hundred and many of them are fitted with elaborate robes and jewelry, some of which are genuine articles. It is a spectacular show, made possible by beeswax—a product that lasts indefinitely. Benjamin Franklin looks as real today as he did the day he posed for Madame Tussaud's in Paris, over 170 years ago.

In normal times the largest users of beeswax are the makers of cosmetics and candles, but during World War II beeswax was an essential war material, needed at the rate of more than a million pounds a year. It had, and still has, over one hundred important military uses, including the coating of shells, bullets, and airplane wings. In fact, every plane to the South Pacific, Europe, Asia, or Africa, carried beeswax to be put to some war use, for there seemed to be no adequate substitute. It was also used in a make-up preparation that made the hands and faces of men in raiding parties less visible.

Dentists use wax in large quantities for the preparation of inlays and other dental fixtures; cobblers rub it on the thread with which they sew shoes. It is used on canvas as waterproofing and as a mildew preventative; it is an ingredient of adhesive tape; it provides better insulation for electric wiring, and it is used to wax cables and pulleys.

From the early Egyptians' wax writing-tablets to this twentieth century of electrical recording, wax has served mankind dramatically and usefully in preserving his writings, thoughts, speech, music, and historic figures.

PROPOLIS

Propolis is another bee-product.   It is a sticky exudation which is gathered by bees from the resinous buds and limbs of trees.   The bees use it to coat the inside of the beehive to make it watertight and airtight, and wherever "gluing" is necessary.   Commerce also makes use of this propolis.   Dissolved in alcohol and filtered, it is used as a varnish and gives a polish to wood and a golden color to tin.   A preparation made with finely ground propolis, gum arabic, incense, storax, sugar, nitre, and charcoal is molded into fumigating cones for perfuming rooms or halls.

MISCELLANEOUS

PROVERBS:

"Busy as a bee."
"What is good for the swarm is not good for the bee."
"Bee in your bonnet."
"Where there is honey, there are bees."
"He who would gather the honey must bear the sting of the bees."
"Who flees the bees runs into the jaws of the lion."
"A drone is one who does not labor."
"Drones suck not eagle's blood but rob beehives."
"From the same flower the bee extracts honey and the wasp gall."
"The bee from his industry in the summer eats honey all the winter."
"One bee is better than a handful of flies."
"His head is full of bees." [A Scotch saying, said of a drunkard.]
"Beeline." [Meaning a direct route.]
"Honey sometimes turns sour."
"The diligence of the hive produces the wealth of honey."
"A drop of honey will not sweeten the ocean."
"If you want to gather honey, don't kick over the beehive."
"Luxury has honey in her mouth, gall in her heart, and sting in her tail."

GENERAL:

Honey. The word "honey" is a term of endearment and the symbol of all that is pure, sweet and wholesome.

A countless number of Asiatics believe that each bee contains the soul of a dead person.

SYMBOLS:

A beehive forms the central motif of the great seal of the State of Utah.

On the roof of a large house in Salt Lake City there is a huge structure that resembles an oversized beehive. This historic place was once the residence of Brigham Young, founder of the Mormon settlement, and is known as "The Beehive House."

On a Continental U.S. forty-five-dollar bill, issued on January 14, 1779, an apiary is represented in which two beehives are visible with the bees swarming about. The motto is "Sic floret Republica" (Thus flourishes the Republic). It conveyed the simple lesson that by industry and frugality the Republic would prosper.

The clock above the entrance to The Bank for Savings in the City of New York is decorated with bees to represent thrift. The corporate seal of the bank is an old-fashioned "skep," with the motto: "The hand of the diligent maketh rich."

Napoleon I (Napoleon Bonaparte) and his nephew Napoleon III (Louis Napoleon) had their imperial robes embroidered with golden bees to symbolize their claim of descent from Carolus Magnus who reportedly wore them on his coat-of-arms.

Chapter VII

The Socializers

The Ants

The enormous number of ants, and their wide distribution, probably make them the most familiar of all insects, with the possible exception of the common housefly. Professor William Morton Wheeler, who tirelessly investigated ants for many years, said: "Ants are to be found everywhere, from the Arctic regions to the tropics, from the timberline of the loftiest mountains to the shifting sands of dunes and seashores, and from the dampest forests to the driest deserts."

The ants also belong in the Order Hymenoptera. They are all social insects, living in colonies where there is a true division of labor. In each colony the members consist of the males, the females, and the workers. The workers, which are the ones ordinarily seen, never have wings and as a rule are sterile females. Upon them devolves all the labor of a colony. These workers may be more than one size and some may be differentiated as "soldiers."

Very often, in the spring and in the summer of the year, large numbers of winged ants may be seen swarming about. These are the recently matured sexual forms (both males and females) that possess wings for only the short time until they have completed their mating flights. Upon mating, the males die and the females, now queens, usually proceed to break off their wings and seek out small cavities in which to found new colonies. After closing the entrance a queen remains alone and without food for weeks or months, during which time she lays her first eggs. The larvae hatching from these first eggs she feeds with her saliva. When this first brood matures the adults are small, due to the limited supply of food. These are the first workers and they care for succeeding broods, which are larger in size because they are better nourished. The first brood is the only one the queen nurses; thereafter she becomes an egg-laying organism for her colony. She is not the ruler, but the mother of the colony. The workers, guided by instinct, take over the duties of the nest; they care for the young, build new galleries, forage for food, and keep the nest clean. The eggs and immature young are kept in chambers of the nest but may be carried about by the workers to take advantage of changes in temperature and moisture. They are moved near the surface during the warmer part of the day and removed to deeper chambers at night or during rainy weather. The "ant eggs" sold for feeding birds and fishes are not ant eggs but the immature young, or pupae—the stage immediately preceding their emergence as adults.

FIGURE 20. As the Word "ant" is Written in Japanese The character on the extreme left represents "insect." When this is combined with the characters designating "unselfishness," "justice," and "courtesy," the whole makes up the Japanese ideogram for "ant"—and the flattering opinion the Japanese hold for it.

The so-called army or legionary ants of tropical and subtropical America are probably the most feared of all their kind. In contrast to most ants that have permanent nests, the army ants live in temporary nests and travel on cloudy days or at night in immense "armies" of hundreds of thousands. They consume all the animal refuse in their way, devour all the insects they meet, and will not hesitate to attack all kinds of vertebrates, including human beings. When they are "on the march" animals flee from their unswerving path. They even enter houses, leaving them as free of dirt and vermin as the proverbial Dutch kitchen.

The laborious life and "foresight" of the ant have been celebrated for centuries and many a sluggard has been referred to this insect "to learn her ways and be wise." The Arabians customarily would place an ant in the hands of a newborn infant, and repeat the words: "May the boy turn out clever and skillful." The ways and uses of these insects are indeed a fascinating subject to study.

In early medical literature there are numerous references to the use of black ants for closing incisions and small perforations, as well as for stitching extensive wounds. Some references date back to Hindu writings as early as 1000 B.C. The large black ants, the "Carpenter ants" and some of their near relatives, possess powerful jaws with which they are able to grasp objects with extraordinary firmness. To effect a suture, an ant is so placed that when its wide open jaws snap shut, upon contact with the skin, the edges of the skin are held snugly together. The ant's body is then pinched off and the saw-toothed jaws remain firmly attached until the wound heals. In this manner, by using a number of ants, a sizable cut may be sutured. Dr. Eugene Gudger (1925) says that the use of ants for suturing among civilized people is confined to the circle of the Mediterranean: "Spain, France, Italy, in former times; Algeria, Asia Minor, and Dalmatia in recent days—warm regions where ants abound and where they may be obtained throughout the greater part of the year."

In Guiana, another species of jungle ant used for stitching wounds is called "kushi." (The generic name for this ant is *Atta*.) In a colony of this species there are soldier ants whose function is protection of the nest from enemy invasion. These soldier ants have very prominent, scissor-shaped, saw-toothed jaws which grip anything that comes within their reach. Even after the ant has been beheaded it is not easy to loosen its bulldog grip. Natives living along the Amazon have noted this tenacity and make use of these ants whenever deep wounds are incurred. They have no modern medical equipment for stitching wounds but they effect perfect sutures by this primitive method of "clamp-stitching."

The *Atta* is commonly called the "parasol ant," or the "leaf-cutting" ant. These common names are derived from their habit of cutting small pieces from leaves and carrying them over their heads. The ants are actually hidden by the comparatively large bits of leaves they carry in firmly clasped jaws, so that a procession of workers returning to the nest presents a very curious appearance indeed—they make the floor of the jungle look as if it had come to life. These bits of leaves are not held overhead to shade the ants from the sun, because the sun seldom penetrates to the floor of the jungle where these insects live. Neither are they eaten as food, although they are used in producing food for the colony. The worker ants chew these leaf fragments into a mulchlike mass and deposit it in the underground chambers of the nest. There, fungus is grown upon this deposit from spores which are planted and cultivated by the worker ants. The fungus grows in knobby lumps, producing thousands of little, juicy, fruiting bodies which are then eaten as food by the ant colony.

Often, a path to and from the leaf source becomes a miniature highway. In a large and active nest, the ants traveling this path little by little pick up all loose bits of twigs, dead leaves, small pebbles, grass and weeds, and simply dump them to either side, leaving bare a main track six to eight inches wide. After countless thousands of ant-hours of labor this "highway" appears as smooth and is as firm as if it had been made by a broad, heavy wheel.

In 1938 the late Doctor Raymond Ditmars returned from Trinidad with a nuclear nest of parasol ants—a queen with some of her soldiers and workers and a small section of the fungus garden—which he earnestly desired to exhibit alive in the New York Zoological Gardens in Bronx Park. Dr. Ditmars also brought back a supply of their native food plants, but the problem of what to feed these ants, once this food supply became exhausted, assumed serious proportions as each kind of leaf in the Botanical Gardens was rejected by the ants for the growing of their fungus gardens. Finally, at someone's suggestion, rose petals were tried. The ants eagerly cut these up and carried them into their nest, and ever since rose petals have been provided for them daily. Later, sliced grapefruit and oranges were introduced and the pulpy cells of these fruits were also accepted for the raising of their fungus.

Parasol ants are used as food by almost all the Indians of the Amazon, as well as by the Indians of the Mosquito Coast of Honduras. They are collected at the beginning of the rainy season, when the swarming winged ants emerge from their nests. The Indians make miniature dirigible-shaped baskets which they hold against the exits of the nests so that the ants fall into them as they emerge. The worker ants and the soldier ants, which have sharp spines on the neck and head, are usually avoided as food by the natives.

The head-hunting Jivaros Indians of South America call these "winged" ants *uku* and eat them raw. The Jicaque Indians of Central America call them *ara* but while they also eat the entire insects they cook them first. The Miskito Indians of the Mosquito Coast of Honduras pull off the heads, legs, and wings, and then toast the bodies only. The flavor, when thus prepared, is said to have a pungent, oily taste, not unlike crisped bacon.

Other interesting ants, belonging to a group commonly known as honey ants (of the genus *Myrmecocystus*), have also played an important role as one of the foods of various aborigines. These insects have received the name of honey ants from the remarkable fact that some of the workers function as honey-pots, or reservoirs for storing honeydew gathered by other worker ants. Nests or colonies of these ants, each nest containing a queen, the workers, and the honey-bearers, are usually found near scrub oak where the workers collect nectar from nectar-excreting abnormal growths, or "galls," on the trees. They swallow the nectar and carry it to their nest in their crops, whereupon they regurgitate it and feed it to the workers in which the honey is stored—in much the same way as honey is stored by bees in the honeycombs of their beehive. The workers that serve to store the honey are known as *rotunds* or *repletes* because their distended abdomens are used as honey-sacs. They are overfed by the ordinary workers and in this way act as living barrels of stored food, sometimes becoming distended to the size of a very small grape. These *rotunds* always remain in special chambers—twenty-five to thirty in each chamber of an ant nest, clinging to the ceiling with their feet and powerless to move from place to place. As many as 250 to 300 *rotunds* may be found in the several chambers of a single nest. As they cling to the ceiling they look like a cluster of very small, semi-transparent grapes, and if one happens to fall it is assisted to its former position by the workers. The honey in these honey-pots is about eight times the weight of the ant, twelve hundred of them weighing one pound, whereas ten thousand ordinary workers are required to equal the same weight. During the winter, or in the barren season, the ordinary workers visit the *rotunds* for their daily food. The worker places its mouth to that of the *rotund* and the *rotund*

FIGURE 21. **Honey Ants** A small cluster of overfed honey ants—living containers of honey—clinging to the ceiling of the nest. The honey ant at the lower left is in the process of being overfed preparatory to being assisted to the ceiling.

contracts the muscles of her honey-sac, thereby squeezing forth a tiny droplet of honey that is immediately consumed by the worker.

The Australian aborigines use these ants to get a refreshing drink by biting off the honey-distended abdomen and crushing out the honey. They then discard the chitinous covering, much as one would discard the skin of a grape.

The Indians of Mexico and the southwestern United States dig up colonies of honey ants just to collect the *rotunds*. They then press out the honey and eat it in preference to bee honey. Sometimes these honey ants are crushed and applied to wounds as a poultice and when so used are considered to be a healing application of great effectiveness.

Ants are known to have an acute sense of "smell." When an ant locates food, her excitement causes her to exude minute droplets of formic acid, which in turn attract and excite other members of her colony. Thus a regular trail is formed between the nest and the food source. The ants pick up this trail and follow it by their sense of smell, which, it is believed, is situated in their antennae. Insects do not have noses and it is supposed that it is primarily through their antennae, equipped with sense hairs and spines, that they react to outside stimuli such as touch, smell, taste and hearing.

Anthropological literature contains the following story of how the first ants originated and how they came to have such a keen sense of smell. A villager who was accustomed to having pranks played upon him came home one evening and decided to turn the tables on the pranksters, so he professed to have an exceptionally keen sense of smell. As soon as he made his boast his friends decided to disprove it. They tested him on four jars containing food and by sheer coincidence he correctly guessed their contents to be of flesh, fish, honey, and oil. His fame to "smell out" anything soon spread, until finally the King called for him and commanded him to find his lost pearl—or lose his head! While bemoaning his plight he accidentally came upon the thieves who had, by this time, become quite frightened. He was therefore easily able to persuade them to give him the pearl, whereupon he returned it to the King. Three days thereafter the Queen summoned him to tell her what was in a box, the contents of which she alone knew. In his bewilderment he muttered an old saying: "The bagged cat soon dies." The Queen asked him to repeat it louder and he was just as amazed as the others present, although he concealed his amazement, to learn that she had placed a cat in the box. Thereupon the people cried, "He is not a man, he is a god!" So they threw him up into the sky to live among the gods. When he was tossed into the sky he held a handful of earth, and when he disappeared the earth fell back. But it was no longer a handful of earth, it was a handful of ants! The story claims that it is because the ants fell from the hands of this man that they have such a wonderful sense of smell.

Formic acid is the active substance of the sting of the ant as well as the source of a scent which attracts other ants. It has long been considered to have medicinal value. One of the remedies for rheumatics, *Spiritus formicarum* or *Spirit of ants* as it was designated in books of pharmacy, was made by crushing two parts of the little red ant (*Formica rufa*) in three parts of alcohol, this being filtered before use. A Russian remedy for rheumatics was the liberation of formic acid from the ants by pouring boiling water over an anthill. It would be interesting to know just how a Russian took this treatment but unfortunately that is not stated. The oil of another species of ant (*Formica sp.*), obtained by infusion, was said to be good for gout and palsy. In Maine the lumbermen eat the large black ants found in pine trees as a means of preventing scurvy. In the Ozarks, the big black ants (probably carpenter ants) were dried and powdered and then mixed with lard. This mixture was rubbed on the legs of babies having weak legs, and on the legs of babies who were slow in learning to walk.

In the Pomeroon District of Guiana the ant holds an important place in the tribal customs of the Arawak Indians. These Indians are introduced to the bite of an ant at about the time they begin to walk. At that tender age the mother will place a small biting ant on her child in the belief that the ant's bite will stimulate her offspring to learn to walk quickly.

The Arawaks believe that when walking along a pathway in the woods, one must not mind and must not harm "munirikuti" (the Arawak name for a species of black ant) should it bite the foot. They say that if such a thing happens it is an omen that betokens something very good and satisfying to the person bitten.

Indians in this tribe voluntarily submit to various painful ordeals or "preparatory charms" prior to setting out on a chase. One ordeal consists of "mortification of the flesh" by ants. This is accomplished in the following manner: an Indian makes a small mat about six to eight inches square, using narrow strips of integument from a reedlike plant, and these strips are tied together somewhat as are the laths of a Venetian blind. Rows of ants are placed between each pair of strips so that they cannot extricate themselves. Their heads, which are placed so that they all project from one side of the mat, are freely movable. The huntsman then presses the side of the mat from which these heads project against his bare chest and permits the ants to bite him mercilessly. By this ordeal he believes he will win success in the chase.

Among the Arawaks the young people of both sexes cannot marry until they have undergone "the ordeal of the ants." Every member of the tribe, upon reaching puberty, must pass this test. When an Arawak girl attains womanhood an "ant-frame" is placed on her head, hands, and feet. The placing is always done by some old and highly esteemed tribesman who must be in no way related to the individual. It is believed that passing this test of fortitude is evidence that henceforth a girl will have the strength and willingness to work. A boy is subjected to the same ordeal in the belief that it will render him skillful, clever, and industrious. The ordeal is so severe that some do not survive it.

There are a number of other odd beliefs about ants. Their actions are sometimes associated with changing weather conditions. Rain is predicted when ants withdraw into their nests "to busy themselves with their eggs." One of the most widespread superstitions is that stepping on an ant will bring rain. In Mexico, along the Rio Grande, winged ants coming out of an anthill are a forecast of heavy showers. The Mexicans claim the winged ants fly out to escape drowning and that the wingless ants remaining in the hill are drowned. Actually, the flying ants are sexually mature forms possessing wings only for the duration of their swarming or mating period when they leave the old nest to establish new ones.

In certain rural sections cornbread crumbs are placed around the cucumber plants because of the belief that the crumbs attract ants which in turn kill destructive cucumber insects.

In Louisiana we find the superstition that ridding the house of ants can be accomplished either by throwing coffee grounds under the kitchen steps, or, if not on the best of terms with your next door neighbor, by rolling four or five of the troublesome ants in a leaf, and carrying them to the neighbor's house. The supposition is that all the ants will leave your house and go to his.

MISCELLANEOUS

PROVERBS:

"What would the ant do if she but had the head of a bull."
"Go to the ant thou sluggard, consider her ways and be wise."

"A coconut shell full of water is an ocean to an ant."

"Even an emmet (ant) may seek revenge."

"An emmet may work its heart out, but cannot make honey."

"Even an ant is eight spans long as measured by its own hand."

"None preaches better than the ant and she says nothing."

"God gives wings to the ant that she may perish the sooner."

"The ant has wings to its hurt."

"Ants never bend their course to an empty granary."

"Ants take over all de grease." Trinidad proverb. [When people quarrel, strangers come to know their business, hence this is an admonition to keep quiet.]

GENERAL:

Stepping on an ant brings rain.

SYMBOL:

Epigram of an ant enclosed in amber:

> "A drop of amber from the weeping plant,
> Fell unexpected and embalmed an ant;
> The little insect we so much condemn,
> Is, from a worthless ant, become a gem."

Chapter VIII

Insect Anesthetizers

The Hornets and Wasps

Hornets and wasps are much alike in characteristics although there are thousands of different species, but for the layman's better understanding, and generally speaking, they are *all* wasps—the larger forms usually being called hornets.   Like the bees and the ants they belong to the Order Hymenoptera.

These insects have long been noted for the characteristic manner in

117

which they sting their prey, some other insect or a spider, in order to provision their nests. Their prey is paralyzed, but remains alive and in a preserved condition for a period of several weeks. Not until the mother hornet or wasp has provisioned her cell will she lay her egg, and this she does upon the immobilized body of her victim. She then closes the cell from the outside for she has completed her mission. Within this cell the egg hatches and the larva immediately proceeds to feed upon the food left therein. By the time the freshly preserved victim is consumed, the still immature wasp or hornet has formed a little cocoon, inside of which development is completed before it emerges as an adult. It then burrows its way out of the ground.

In the case of the "social" hornets and wasps which live in community nests, a young fertilized queen is the only one that lives through the winter. Subject to the laws of nature, the others in the nest die at the approach of cold weather. The queen hibernates during the winter and in the spring emerges from hibernation to start a new nest. The elaborate nests of hornets and wasps are often made of paper which they produce themselves by chewing wood pulp mixed with their own saliva. Nearly every oldtime cabin has one of these empty nests hanging up in the loft in the belief that it will be the means of bringing good fortune to the entire household, and the Ozark girls once carried little wasp nests pinned to their undergarments in the belief that this concealed nest would make them attractive to men.

Wasps that use mud to build their nests are commonly called "dirt daubers." From the south comes the story that when Dirt Dauber first started to build her house, Hornet offered to show her how to build it. But Dirt Dauber refused aid, insisting that she knew "how to do it." When all but the door was finished, Hornet came again to show how the door should be fastened on. Dirt Dauber again refused aid, went inside, put on the door, fastened it from the inside, and then daubed it up so that it was impossible for her to come out! In this manner she came to an untimely end. The story claims that dirt daubers build their nests in sections, the way hornets do, but that inside of each section the shell of a dead dirt dauber will be found.

For this reason, in the south, when someone of questionable ability boastfully insists that he knows "how to do it," he is sarcastically referred to as a "dirt dauber."

Hornets and wasps apparently have not been used as extensively as bees and ants in effecting cures. One cure from Ohio suggested that hornets' nests made into a poultice would relieve rheumatism, and another cure from Kentucky advocated the use of a poultice made from mud daubers' nest to treat boils.

The Kwakiutl Indians of our northwest coast are said to successfully cure a severe headache by means of cauterization. For this purpose a mixture of nettle fibre and a wasp nest is made into a small ball. Then the ball, held by a pair of tongs, is ignited and applied to the temples, to the nape of the neck, and to the crown of the head. The reason why this treatment works seems obvious; the pain from the burns is so intense that the poor victim forgets all about his headache!

A common superstition is that the severity of the coming winter may be determined by the height at which hornets build their nests. If built low, it is said that the winter will be cold. On the other hand, if they are observed high up, a mild winter is predicted. According to some southern Negroes, if a dirt dauber builds close to the ground, there will be a dry year, but if they build up high—look out for lots of rain. An entomologist, however, would account for the difference in heights at which hornets and wasps build their nests with the explanation that some species habitually seek high sites, while other species habitually seek low sites.

In Maryland they tell a story about a hornet's nest and the time a British vessel, said to have been a flagship, sailed up the Patuxent River during the war of 1812 and dropped anchor off Lower Marlboro. The officers went ashore to see something of the land of the Yankees. They were taking a walk through the woods and fields when they came upon a hornets' nest. Not knowing what it was, they called out to a young boy who was playing nearby and asked him. Recognizing the officers to be enemies of his country, the boy declared that the hornets' nest was actually the nest of a rare hummingbird and said: "If you stop up the hole at the bottom and take the nest out to sea, perhaps about ten miles, you will have a couple of little birds that will stay with the ship as mascots." A short time later the flagship weighed anchor and went down the Patuxent with the tide. What happened is still based upon conjecture and report, although "Uncle George" Younger, who had told the story, never intimated that there was the slightest doubt about it. The plug must have been withdrawn according to the boy's directions because that day, about sunset, several of Lower Marlboro's residents, watching through glasses, saw Admiral Cockburn and a dozen of his officers dive overboard into the bay— swords and all! The *Calvert Independent*, a newspaper published in Barstow, Maryland, referred to this incident in 1941, recalling it in a verse by Ralph Hinman who had heard "Uncle George's" way of telling it:

> The hornets surely won the day,
> And made their foes feel shame;
> These insects were American
> And lived up to their name!

Another insect, noted for its potent and very painful sting, is the "velvet ant," which is also called the "woolly ant," "mule killer," "cow ant," or "cow killer," depending on the section of the country. However, this insect is *not* an ant, but a mutillid wasp. It probably got the name "velvet ant" because the female is wingless and looks like an ant that is covered with a velvety pubescence which is often a brilliant red or yellow. They are parasitic on bees and other wasps. The males, which are winged, spend most of their time frequenting flowers. Once again, it is the female which possesses the powerful sting; the males are not known to sting.

It is in the southern part of the United States that this insect is known as the "cow killer," because of the popular superstition that its sting is dangerous to livestock. While it does terrify livestock to the point of causing self-injury by erratic behavior, such as dashing away blindly, the sting itself is not lethal.

The Cherokees call it *da sûn tali atatsûn ski* ("stinging ant") and sometimes, because of its hard body case, it is called *nûn yunú wi* ("stone dress") after a celebrated Cherokee mythical monster. The chitinous body covering of these mutillids is so hard that even an entomologist, using a sharp, steel pin, has difficulty in piercing the thorax when pinning it for study.

In the Orient, certain species of mutillid wasps are used by physicians for treating snake bites, and by veterinarians for treating colic in horses.   At the other extreme, in the region of the Amazon River, the Canelos, a tribe of headhunters, associate the poisonous stings inflicted by "yutúri supai" (a black wasp) and "tucandeira" (a black ponerine ant) with "invisible magic arrows."   They believe that their witch doctors have the power to use these "invisible arrows" for bewitching tribesmen. These headhunters regard all poisonous insects as demons.

MISCELLANEOUS

PROVERBS:

"As mad as a hornet."
"Stirring up a hornets' nest."

GENERAL:

If a wasp flies into the house, good luck will follow.
Wasp waist.

FIGURE 22.

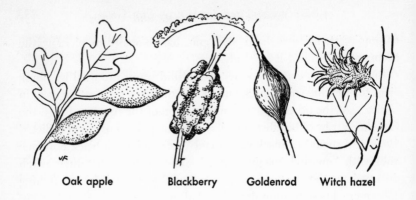

| Oak apple | Blackberry | Goldenrod | Witch hazel |

Chapter IX

Cancerlike Plant Growths

The Galls

Galls have been mentioned in relating the story of the honey-ant. They are abnormal growths on plants, bushes, or trees and they have the appearance of warts, nuts, or swellings. They are caused *primarily* by insect-injury to the tender parts of leaves, roots, or stems. These odd, nectar-excreting growths which one may see on any country jaunt are of importance in the scheme of nature. The insect gall-makers are the flies, the bees and wasps, the beetles, the bugs, and a few moths, but not the butterflies. Some galls are caused by fungi, others by mites. While galls differ in shape, the form of the gall is remarkably constant *for each species of gall-making insect.* Some entomologists are of the opinion that injuries caused by the insertion of insect eggs are sufficient to initiate this rapid localized growth, whereas others think a gall is the result of the internal irritation of plant tissues by developing larvae. In either case, irritation is the stimulus causing excessive cell multiplication, and the resulting abnormal growth.

Some of the most attractive-looking galls are to be found on rose leaves which have been attacked by gall wasps. Such galls are known

122

as "robins' pincushion," "moss gall," or "bedeguar gall." The curious word "bedeguar" is said to be derived either from the Persian and Arabic *badawar*, meaning "wind-brought," or to be a compound of the Persian *bād*, meaning "wind," and the Arabic word *ward*, meaning "rose."

The most common of the galls are the goldenrod galls produced by tiny flies known as gall midges. In some localities, especially in damp, sandy places, galls are so abundant on goldenrod that one could easily collect two or three hundred in a few hours. It is believed that the goldenrod gall gets its start when the female gall midge lays a single egg upon the stem of the goldenrod at about the time the plant is two or three feet high. When the young grub hatches, it burrows its way into the center of the goldenrod stem. The larva feeds upon the abundant supply of food within the gall as the gall continues to grow. Then, when winter approaches, the goldenrod stem and the gall which has formed upon it harden to form a tough chamber in which the insect safely passes the winter. Sometime during the fall or winter the larva changes to a pupa and awaits the coming of spring to emerge, which it does either by boring or eating its way out of the chamber.

In the Middle Ages the ignorance of the origin of galls gave rise to many queer notions and superstitious practices. At that time galls were gravely recorded as supernatural growths and were employed as a means of foretelling the events of the coming year. The gall, upon being opened, was supposed to contain a maggot, a fly, or a spider. If it was a maggot it betokened that the coming year would bring famine; if a fly it forecast war; and if a spider, pestilence. This belief was recorded and practiced for several centuries, even after the true relationship of the plant and insect was established. Today a slightly different version of this belief is prevalent. If an oak gall, or "oak apple" as it is sometimes called, is cut open in the fall of the year, one of three things will be found in it: a fly—denoting want, a worm—denoting plenty, or a spider—denoting death.

The observations of the practical use of galls that have come down to us from the old physicians and naturalists of Greece and Rome were confined chiefly to the Aleppo gall of the oak tree and the Bedeguar gall of the rose, and it is interesting to note that much of the data of that period was recorded by the light of these two particular galls because the ancients burned them in their lamps in place of oil.

Like most other vegetable substances, galls were used medicinally as early as the fifth century B.C. Pliny recorded that twenty-three remedies were compounded of gall nuts. Among other things they were prescribed for ulcerations of the mouth, affections of the gums, malformed nails, hangnails, and burns. Now, over two thousand years later, we find that as an astringent for burns the Aleppo gall is listed in the U.S. Pharmacopoeia as a source of tannic acid and as the principal ingredient in the preparation of *Unguentum gallae*, which is used externally, especially for burns. Pliny also mentioned that when powdered and mixed with honey and applied to the head galls were successful in restoring hair, and at one time, in Italy, a powdered form was applied to counteract the bites of venomous animals.

In London, about the middle of the last century, galls were recommended as a tonic in intermittent fevers, as a chemical antidote, as a topical or local astringent, and as an astringent in hemorrhages. For use in hemorrhages, until comparatively recent times, galls were considered efficacious in effecting blood clotting if merely carried in the pocket! They were also used in Europe as a cure for fevers; and to relieve toothache the inner part of the gall was chewed.

Galls are used as food in some places. In Mexico City, for example, they may often be found on fruit stands. Some galls are said to be sweeter than sugar. From Missouri comes the report that one of the local galls is so abundant that it is fed to cattle, hogs, sheep, and poultry. These animals are said to be very fond of them and it is claimed that they actually get fat on this diet. Verification of this claim comes from Arkansas where local galls are fed mostly to hogs.

In the literature relating to the history of the art of dyeing, the Aleppo gall figures prominently from the earliest mention of the art up to the present time. As an article of commerce, therefore, this gall has the longest history for it was used by the Greeks in dyeing wool and woolen goods, and Pliny mentioned it as being used to stain the hair black. In addition to being known as Aleppo gall it is also known as Turkey gall, Levant gall, gall of commerce, and ink marble. It is found on oak trees in eastern Europe and in western Asia, and it has long been considered a necessary ingredient in the manufacture of non-fading inks. In some countries the law requires that court records be made with ink compounded from this gall. It is also specified in the formulae for inks used by the United States Treasury, the Bank of England, the German Chancellory, and the Danish Government.

A gall somewhat resembling the Aleppo gall and often confused with it is caused by a small wasp. This gall, known as the "mad apple of Sodom," "Dead Sea fruit," "Mecca," or the "Bussorah" gall, is found on low oaks growing on the borders of the Dead Sea. In this region it was preferred for use as a dye (mixed with cochineal and tartar) to attain the color known as Turkey red. The widespread use of gall nuts as the basic ingredient of dyes extends to the Somali women of East Africa, who traditionally use local species to produce their tattooing dye.

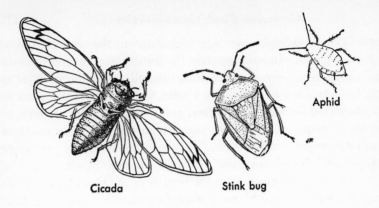

Cicada   Stink bug   Aphid

Chapter X

Insect Hypodermics

The Bugs

Those who have not studied entomology are apt to apply the term "bug" to all kinds of insects. However, it is well to bear in mind the old entomological maxim that all bugs are insects, but all insects are not bugs. Strictly speaking, only members of the Order Hemiptera are bugs, the best known being the aphids (plant lice), cicadas (harvest flies), bedbugs, stinkbugs, leaf hoppers, and water boatmen. Green is the prevailing color of bugs but in certain species they may be more conspicuously colored.

The name "Hemiptera" means "half-wings" (*Hemi* = half; *ptera* = wings) and was given to this group of insects because in many of them the front parts of the front pair of wings are thick, while the remaining parts of the front wings as well as the hind wings are so thin that at a glance they look like half wings. Some recent authorities are inclined to divide the Order Hemiptera into two suborders—Heteroptera and Homoptera—but there is no general agreement on this point.

Bugs are generally plant feeders and commonly abound on grass and foliage, although some species live in, or on the surface of the water, while others are parasitic on birds and mammals. The young usually resemble the parents from the moment of hatching (incomplete metamorphosis) and feed in a manner similar to the adults; all of them, young and adults alike, live by piercing either plant or animal tissue. Their food always consists of fluids—either sap or blood. They are transmitters of virus and other diseases among plants and animals and because of the vast amount of injury they cause to vegetation no other group of insects so directly affects human economy.

CICADAS

The loudest sounding and probably the best known of the "noise-making" bugs is the Cicada or harvest fly. It is this insect that is erroneously called "locust." The true locusts, as previously explained, belong to the Order Orthoptera. The term "locust" was doubtlessly applied to this species because it appeared in great swarms and reminded early observers in this country of the hordes of migratory locusts, or grasshoppers, of the Old World.

When a certain species of cicada (probably *Tibicen linnei*) with a pronounced letter "W" showing on the wings emerges in great numbers it is generally believed to forecast a war. There is really nothing mystical about this because in *Tibicen linnei* (and probably in other allied species) the "W" is the normal pattern of pigmentation where certain veins of the wings come together.

The cicada has one formidable enemy—the large, ferocious hornet called the cicada killer (*Sphecius speciosus*). This hornet paralyzes the cicada with her sting, and although smaller, has the strength to carry the cicada to her burrow where she places it on its back and lays her egg on its underside as a measure of providing food for the larva which will hatch from the egg.

One of the best known species of cicada is the periodical cicada of North America (*Magicicada septendecim*), often known as the "seventeen-year locust" because the young need approximately seventeen years to complete their development. The seventeen-year broods occur in the northern states, but there is a southern variety of this cicada that has a thirteen-year development cycle. The eggs are laid within twigs in slits made by the female, and upon hatching the young nymphs drop to the ground and proceed to bury themselves.   During this long period their food consists of the juices that they suck from the roots of trees.   Finally, after sixteen summers below the ground for the "seventeen-year locust," or twelve summers in the ground for the southern variety, they are ready to emerge as adults.   As the time of emergence approaches they dig upward by means of enlarged front feet. When they come up out of the ground they fasten themselves to some support and their skins split.   Then, as they laboriously pull themselves from their old skins, the soft, creamy-white cicadas with prominent red eyes appear.   Within a few hours the air has two effects—it hardens the body-covering and darkens the color to black and green. The empty pupal skins remain hanging upon the trunks of trees or other places in great numbers.

The Oraibi Indians' observation of the cicada's life cycle was basic to the formulation of their belief that this insect symbolizes resurrection.   They were particularly impressed by the series of physical changes which they noted, especially the splitting of the skin, the emergence of a "white" insect, the change in coloration, and the empty skin left behind when the insect flew away.   These Indians call the cicada "white locust" which, they say, was the color of the first locust that came forth with their early ancestors.   They claim that it dies and returns to life as a black insect, and that since it has the power to renew

its own life, a medicine made from its body has the power to renew the life of others. For this reason, when mortal wounds were received in battle, a medicine made from these insects was used in the belief that it had the power of regeneration.

The Japanese, too, have an unusual appreciation of the cicada.   They make an exquisitely formed, beautifully painted kite, in the conventionalized likeness of the cicada, which they customarily fly in contests at their New Year festivals.   The contestants devote considerable time to constructing their own

FIGURE 23.   A Cicada Kite

kites and take great pride in their craftsmanship. The kites are large (at least three feet in length) and their original designs are based upon objects in the natural world such as plants and animals—for instance, a leaf, a bird, a lizard, or a cicada. Although these kites are delicately constructed of bamboo and rice paper they are exceedingly strong and they are among the best fliers of their kind.

In China's ancient religion the death rite customarily included the placing of certain carved jade amulets at each opening of the body. The superstition was that by closing up all body apertures by means of jade, the evil spirits would be prevented from entering. There were ear amulets, nasal amulets, and so forth, and a tongue amulet which was placed in the mouth. The tongue amulet always was given the wonderful likeness of a cicada which, interestingly, also conformed to the outline of the tongue. The color of the jade selected for carving tongue amulets was usually brown. Jade symbolized the essence of the *yang* element which was to triumph over the destructive evil agencies of the *yin* element, while the likeness of the cicada was the emblem of resurrection. Princes observed the custom of offering such amulets upon the death of persons of equal rank. It was considered the last high honor possible to bestow on a deceased friend.

FIGURE 24. Chinese Tongue Amulet A likeness of the cicada carved in brown jade in use during the Han Dynasty (206 B.C.– 220 A.D.). This is one of the tongue amulets which was placed on the tongue of the dead and buried with the body.

Although it is recorded that the ancient Greeks used cicadas as food, the only known present-day use as food is among the southern Siamese. Their method of attracting cicadas is most unusual. When darkness falls a fire is lighted and the cicada-hunters sit around it. They then clap their hands in unison and before long *female* cicadas arrive in swarms, but how they are then collected is not recorded. Female cicadas are attracted by the clapping but it is not definitely known why. One theory to explain this is based upon the attraction of sexes by vibration.

Our Cherokee Indians call the cicada the jarfly. In midsummer, when it begins to "sing," they say: "The jarfly has brought the beans." The cicada is heard around the middle of the summer at about the time the first crop of beans is ripening. Throughout the United States the song of the cicada is taken as a sign of change of weather. In many rural communities it is said to herald the approach of dry conditions but in the south it is considered to herald inclement weather. The prevalent belief is that when one hears the cicadas sing the next day will be hot.

The Chinese held cicadas in high esteem for the sake of their songs, and as we keep canaries in cages, they kept *male* cicadas in cages. (Female cicadas do not "sing.") The principle of the musical organ of the cicada is that of a vibrating drum. Prolonged shrill notes are emitted by the males and the sound is produced by powerful muscles as air passes in and out of spacious air chambers situated on the underside of the cicada's abdomen. In a series of research experiments on the sounds produced by insects, it has been determined that the cicada's "song" is in the key of high C. This conclusion calls to mind a story which originated during a period when superstitions and myths went unchallenged. At the height of Greek civilization there lived two gifted harpists—Eunomis and Aristo. The musical ability of each man was so great that the public sponsored a contest to determine which of the two was the more talented. Aristo, the snob, finished playing his last piece with his usual mastery of technique and left the audience so impressed that they did not believe their favorite, Eunomis, could do better. However, Eunomis played with feeling and understanding and had almost reached the end of his last solo when his high C string snapped suddenly. Although unnerved and heartbroken, Eunomis continued. When he sorely needed the string for his final high C, a cicada flew into the amphitheatre, jumped to Eunomis' harp, and vibrated its "kettle-drums" at the high C pitch. The cicada "put his all" into that one note and Eunomis won the contest! Ever since, the cicada has been the Greek symbol for melody.

Perhaps the most beautiful description of the song of the cicada was penned by the writing-brush of the Chinese poet Ou-yang Hsui, almost nine centuries ago, when, in the hushed courtyard of the Wine Spring Temple, he heard:

"a thing that cried
Upon a tree top, sucking the shrill wind
To wail it back in a long whistling note—
Now shrill as a flute, now soft as a mandolin:
Sometimes a piercing cry
Choked at its very uttering, sometimes a cold tune
Dwindled into silence, then suddenly flowing again,
A single note, wandering in strange keys
An air yet fraught
With undertone of hidden harmony."

FIGURE 25.

There is a small Chinese bug about the size of a housefly that the Chinese persist in calling a cicada. Actually this bug, *Cixius limbata,* is a fulgorid—another kind of bug. This insect exudes a waxy secretion which when melted and purified becomes white and glossy in appearance. The Chinese mix this secretion with oil to make candles of a superior grade, and the same mixture is employed by Chinese physicians as a cure in several diseases.   They also prescribe it as an effective preventative of palpitation, nervousness, and swooning when a person is about to make a public address; an ounce of it taken before ascending the platform supposedly induces self-assurance.

One of the most interesting and remarkable species of cicada in the Orient is *Huechys sanguinea*.   There it is called "chu-ki," and also "The red medicinal cicada."   It has brilliant red and black markings and is the only known cicada used as a blistering agent.

APHIDS

Of concern to everyone who grows trees, vegetables, or flowering plants, are the aphids, commonly called "plant lice."   There are over three hundred known species in North America alone.   Even when fully grown they are tiny insects, on the average no larger than pinheads.   They are eaten and preyed upon (parasitized) by other insects, such as minute wasps, so that under natural conditions they die by countless thousands.   They are so prolific, however, that they continue to effect considerable damage to plants by sheer force of reproductive capacity.

The biology of aphids is so complicated that entomologists know the life cycles of comparatively few species.   Reproduction among the aphids combines cycles of sexual and cycles of asexual reproduction, and the type of reproduction usually determines whether the offspring will be winged or wingless upon reaching maturity.   As far as is known, the aphids eliminate males from all but one of their many generations during the year.   Under laboratory conditions they have been observed to produce ninety-four generations without the birth of a single male. According to Charles Brues (1946) they reproduce without mating "during the warmer parts of the season, producing living young which at birth already contain the growing embryos of the third generation. . . ." Although most often green in color, some are black, brown, yellow, or pinkish-red.   They feed by thrusting their tiny hollow beaks, which resemble miniature hypodermic needles, into plant cells to suck out the sap.

No one has a kind word for aphids.   They are major pests in gardens, orchards, and greenhouses, and often cause serious damage to many kinds of plant life.   However, some insects would put in a good word for them, if they could.   These are certain ants, bees, wasps, and flies which feed on the sweet secretions exuded by the aphids.   Some ants actually carry aphids in their mouths to their nests, and protect and care for them during the long winter months.   In the spring of the following year the ants deposit them on plants upon which the aphids may feed.   Thus the ants assure themselves of a supply of the honey-dew which the aphids exude.

Aphids are commonly milked by ants for their honeydew.   The aphid readily submits to the ant's gentle stroking of her sides, with first one antenna, then with the other—a sort of a seesaw motion, much like the milking of a cow.   This rhythmic stroking causes the honey-dew to exude faster and faster.   The ants lap this up, and several ants in turn may milk the same aphid.   About 30 to 40 drops an hour may be obtained in this way.   When the aphids draw more sweet sap than they actually need the surplus is passed out from their bodies.   It has been determined that this secretion (largely cell sap) is an extract of the juices which the aphids suck from plants and which, after passing through their digestive tract, is deposited on leaves and twigs.   When large numbers of aphids are present, honeydew is discharged in enough quantities to be likened to a rain of honey.   The "manna" of Biblical times was, in all likelihood, honeydew.

At one time countless millions of "minute insects flying in the air" were supposed to have some connection with intestinal worms in man.   Such a calamity was once described as "an easterly wind attended by a blue mist."   In reality this wind was loaded with a species of bluish aphids which, being plant feeders by nature, could not possibly transmit intestinal parasites to man.

SCALE INSECTS

Scale insects vary in size according to species.   Some are no bigger than pinheads while others may reach 25 mm. in length.   From the point of view of utility to man certain scale insects make important contributions to the world's commerce.   The commercially profitable ones are the lac insect *Laccifer lacca*, the cochineal insect *Coccus cacti*, the dye insects *Kermes* and *Margarodes*, and the Chinese wax insect *Ericerus pela*.

LAC

The word lac is derived from the Sanskrit *laksha* and is the same as the Hindu *lakh* meaning "one hundred thousand,"—vividly descriptive of the countless numbers of these insects infesting the trees.

The most commercially important of the scale insects are the females of the lac insect *Laccifer lacca*. These females, which are wingless, yield the stick lac of commerce, a resinous excretion from which many products are manufactured. The males of this species, which are winged, are of no commercial value because they do not produce the resinous excretion.

At a certain time of the year, varying according to the locality, mature female lac insects known to the industry as "brood-lac" adhere to twigs in great numbers. These twigs are cut by native workers and tied to the insects' host trees. Soon, newly hatched lac bugs—as many as one-thousand from each female—emerge and swarm by the millions. They start traveling along the branches of the tree seeking a tender piece of bark on which to settle down and feed. If, within the distance of twelve feet, they do not find a suitable place, they die. Once settled, the insects insert their beaks in the sappy area of the tree (the phloem and xylem layers) where they remain for the rest of their lives sucking out the sap. This sap is chemically transformed internally by the lac insects and exuded from tiny glands as resin (lac) in the form of a globule. This exudation continues until it not only conceals the entire body of the insect beneath but also merges with the lac globules of other nearby lac insects. As the globules merge, a continuous incrustic coating about one-quarter of an inch in thickness is formed over the surface of the twig. This incrustation is the lac harvest.

Lac is the basic ingredient of an amazing list of articles: stiffening agents in the toes and soles of shoes, and in felt, fur, and composition hats; shoe polishes; artificial fruits and flowers; lithographic ink; electrical insulation; protective coverings for wood, paper, metal, fabric, wax emulsions, wood fillers, sealing wax and buttons; glazes on confections; coffee bean burnishing; paints; cements and adhesives; shellac varnishes and moldings; photographic products; phonographic records; playing card finishes; dental plates; pyrotechnics; foundry work and hair dyes.

Although India is considered the leading lac producing country, the actual area in which lac insects thrive is about 2,000 miles wide and 2,000 miles long and sweeps down through India, Burma, Siam, and into China. India and Burma produce over 90 per cent of the world's supply of lac. The present annual crop of lac in these two countries is about 64,000,000 pounds and is valued in excess of $20,000,000.

COCHINEAL

Another scale insect, *Coccus cacti*, produces the dyestuff known as *cochineal*. These insects and the cacti upon which they feed are both native to the Americas.

As cochineal insects require only three months to mature, it is possible to collect a crop of about two hundred pounds of insects per acre each May, July, and October. Each pound contains approximately twenty-five thousand dried insects and it has been estimated that it takes two and four-fifths pounds, or about seventy thousand of them, to produce one pound of cochineal dye. The dried insect looks like a seed about the size of a small B.B. shot. It is shriveled in appearance, with transverse wrinkles, and is generally of a silver-gray color. It is known as the cochineal of commerce and from it are obtained the colors known as carmine and lake. Until the discovery of aniline dyes cochineal was an important source of fast reds and violets.

The Aztecs raised cochineal insects and also exacted them as a medium of tribute for the use of lands under cultivation, and our Pima Indians of southern Arizona and southern California produced a red dye from them. Some European countries imported cactus plants and cochineal insects with the idea of establishing a dye industry, but for some unknown reason the insects died and then the cactus spread with disastrous results.

The United States Dispensatory lists *cochineal* and states that in pharmacy it is employed to color tinctures and tooth powders. It has been prescribed for infants with whooping cough and is said to be effective in neuralgia.

KERMES

Long before the discovery of cochineal dye by Europeans, the brilliant red dye of the Old World was produced from bodies of another scale insect, *Coccus ilicis*, commercially known as *granum tinctorium* or *Kermes* (sometimes spelled *Kermez*).   However, it is most widely known by the name of *Kermes* and this name is used interchangeably to apply either to the insects as a raw product, or to the prepared dyestuff made from these insects.

Many dye chemists believe that the ancient Phoenicians were the first to discover the use to which these insects could be put as a basic ingredient of dyes.   They also believe that the discovery took place in Palestine where the blood-red dye made from them was first known as "Zehori."   The Arabs received the insect from Persia and Armenia under the name of *Kermes* or *Alkermes*.   To the Greeks it was known as *Coccus*.

Coccus ilicis was distributed over such a large area that for nearly 3,000 years it provided the scarlet dye widely used from ancient times until the Middle Ages.   It was the source of one of the dyes used in the drapery of the tabernacle and in the holy garments of the high priests.   Matthew 27:28 records how it was with a crimson robe that the Roman soldiers clothed the Saviour in mockery of his claim to royalty.   The Hebrew word Tôluath was translated as "scarlet" or "crimson," and the full expression is "tôluath shâni" or "worm of crimson."   The "shâni" is probably derived from "Shânâh"—"to shine"— alluding to the bright color of the dye.

Scarlet dye was so highly prized by the Romans that these insects frequently formed part of the tribute exacted from a conquered nation. Thus the people of Spain, after they were conquered by Rome, were compelled to pay one-half of their tribute in *Kermes*.   This old Roman custom was followed during the thirteenth and fourteenth centuries when many feudal landlords and monasteries in Europe accepted *Kermes* in partial payment of rents and taxes. The imperishable reds of the Brussels and other Flemish tapestries were derived from this same insect.

At the present time *Kermes* are still gathered in Europe, India, and Persia where they continue to be utilized as of old in preference to modern dyes.

MARGARODES

The outer coverings of *Margarodes,* a species of tropical scale insect, are the so-called "ground pearls," probably because they are found on the "roots" of certain plants. This scale insect was first used for dye purposes in Germany and in Poland around the twelfth century. Old ecclesiastical records show that in the thirteenth century several German monasteries forced their neighbors to collect them as a contribution. Since this unusual harvest was customarily begun with religious ceremonies on the feast day of St. John, the insects were sometimes known as "St. John's Blood." Every year a considerable quantity was sent to Venice, the center of Christendom, and this practice lasted until about 1797 when the Council of Ten which ruled Venice was overthrown.

CHINESE WAX INSECT

One of the main industries of Chiench'ang Valley of China is the cultivation of the small scale insect *Ericerus pela* which produces the wax known as "peh-la," an exclusive product of China. These insects develop conelike scales which encase the eggs of the next generation. In the spring of each year the insects are gathered from LaShu privet trees, wrapped in leaves, placed in split-bamboo cases, and then, strapped to the backs of runners, are transported a distance of approximately 180 miles through the Tibetan mountain range in six days. As the eggs must be kept cool to prevent hatching, the "wax caravan" as it is called, travels by night and rests during the heat of the day. As soon as the runners arrive in Loshan Province, the leaves in which the eggs are wrapped are removed from the cases and fastened among the branches of trees. Within a few days the larvae hatch, and by the end of two weeks the baby insects begin to crawl out of the leaves and ascend the naked branches where they attach themselves and commence to feed and produce wax. The wax is collected during the month of August. For centuries this wax harvest has had great religious significance, probably because it takes place within sight of Mount Omei-shan, one of the five sacred Buddhist mountains of China. For every pound of insects originally placed upon the trees, four to five pounds of wax are harvested. Then the wax is purified, by heating. The boiled insects which settle to the bottom are fed to swine.

The Chinese have great faith in this white gleaming wax and classify it as an elixir of life. It supposedly makes the "flesh grow, stops bleeding, eases pain, restores strength, braces the nerves and joins broken bones together." In a more practical manner it is used as a sizing agent for paper and cotton, and for lusterizing silk.

Primitive Indian tribes on our own west coast obtained wax from several species of local scale insects and used it to secure the sinew backing of bows and to make baskets watertight. They also chewed it as a gum.

BEDBUGS

The English names for the common bedbug (*Cimex lectularius*) were "chinche," "wall-louse" and just plain "bug." "Bug" is a Celtic word signifying a ghost or goblin, probably because the Celts considered bedbugs terrors of the night. This family of blood-sucking bugs contains not over twenty species in the world, eight of which are recorded from North America. The young, immediately upon hatching, look like smaller editions of their parents. Both young and adult bedbugs feed by sucking blood. At no stage of life do they have wings.

To emphasize their ability to get where there is plenty of food the following verse is widely quoted:

The June bug hath a gaudy wing,
The lightning bug a flame,
The bedbug hath no wings at all
But he gets there just the same.

Bedbugs have in the past been recommended for a great variety of ailments. As an ointment for the eyes, crushed bedbugs mixed with salt and human milk were used. In powdered form they were believed to cure all fevers. For hysteria they were given internally and just the smell of them was considered sufficient to relieve those under hysterical suffocation. Eating seven bedbugs mixed with beans was believed to help those suffering with quartan plague, provided the eating was done before the onset of the attack, and even at the present time in certain areas of Ohio this same mixture is considered good as a cure for chills and fever. At one time bedbugs were also thought to be especially good as neutralizers of serpent venom, that of asps in particular, as well as a useful preventative against all other kinds of poisons.

WATER BOATMEN

Aside from the Cicadas, only one other insect among the bugs provides food. These are certain species called "water-boatmen" which lay eggs in great masses on any submerged object. These bugs are well named for their bodies are keel-shaped, greatly resemble miniature boat hulls, and their legs are used as oars, skillfully propelling them through the water. The Mexicans call them "Axayacat" and have capitalized on their egg-laying habits. They place rush mats in ponds, thus creating an ideal place for the attachment of eggs, which, at the proper time, are collected and sold in the market as "caviar"! These eggs are so small and so light that in a rough estimate there are about 200 million to the pound. The eggs are cleaned and sifted, after which they are put into sacks, like flour, and then sold to the people, who make "hautle"—a slightly acidic, cake or biscuit that has a fish-like taste.

MISCELLANEOUS

PROVERB:

"Snug as a bug in a rug."

GENERAL:

The word "bug" forms the basis for many commonly used slang expressions:

A "bug,"—the common reference to a person who has become a fanatic on a certain subject.

"Bugs" or "buggy"—alluding to a demented person.

"Bug-eyed"—said of one showing eyes bulging with astonishment.

"Bughouse"—meaning an insane asylum.

"Bug juice"—the term applied to strong liquor of an inferior quality.

To dream of bedbugs (in Louisiana) is considered a sure sign of sickness.

In South Africa cicadas are known as Christmas bees because they are most evident at Christmastime.

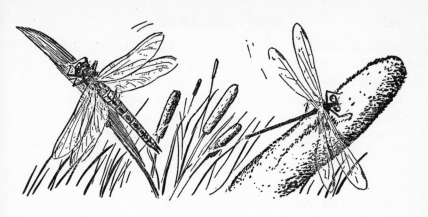

Chapter XI

Master Aerialists

The Dragonflies and the Damselflies

If, on a summer walk, you were to reach the bank of a fresh-water stream, pond, or lake anywhere in our north temperate latitudes, you would be fascinated by the darting flight of "darning needles," "devil's darning needles," "horse stingers," "mosquito hawks," "snake feeders," and "snake doctors." These may be strange names to the reader but they are merely some of the more colorful local names by which dragonflies and damselflies are known. They are members of the Order Odonata and they should be easily recognized by their four gauzy, stiffly outspread wings, their large eyes and heads, and their extremely elongated abdomens. (It is believed that the name Odonata is derived from the Greek word *odon*, meaning "tooth," because of the tusklike appearance of the abdomens of these insects.) Which are the dragonflies and which are the damselflies should also be easily determinable by their differences in size and flight habits. The dragonflies are large and sturdy and their flight is darting and rapid, whereas the damselflies are delicately formed and fly more slowly. Another distinguishing feature is that when at rest the wings of the dragonflies

141

remain extended at right angles to the body, while the damselflies bring their wings together over the body or overlap them parallel to the body.   Although many species are represented in these two groups, the fact remains that they are commonly referred to as "dragonflies." So, in order to avoid confusion, general usage will be followed and all dragonflies and damselflies will be called "dragonflies" in the following pages.

Dragonflies usually attract attention by the lovely color of their two pairs of strongly built cellophanelike wings, reinforced with numerous veins and cross-veins.   They are extremely fast fliers, the larger species having been estimated to travel at approximately sixty miles an hour. They possess the power of great maneuverability, and even when travelling at top speed can abruptly change their course or stop quickly to alight upon a blade of grass or to hover above water.

Strangely enough, although dragonflies are "master aerialists" they must spend the greater part of their lives in water in order to complete their development.   And because water is imperative for full development the female attaches her eggs to aquatic plants beneath the surface of the water, or drops them freely in the water as she flies over it.   The young that hatch are short, flattened, gill-breathing creatures that crawl about in the mud or on aquatic plants in search of food, which consists of smaller aquatic insects.   When about ready to transform into adults, these larvae crawl above the surface of the water and cling to some support for several hours until they emerge from their larval skins; then they are ready for an aerial life.   In some of the smaller species the cycle from the egg to adult may be completed within a year.   In larger species this process may take up to three years.   Although dragonflies are aquatic in their larval stages, once they have developed into adults they are by no means confined to the vicinity of water.   In their adult, winged stage, they are essentially sun-loving insects.

The manner in which a dragonfly captures its prey is most unusual. It forms its six legs into the shape of a basket and into the trap thus formed it scoops its prey while in flight.   This, probably, is why the dragonfly has earned the nickname of "Mosquito Hawk."   Interestingly enough, the dragonfly does not use its legs for the purpose of walking, but primarily for the purpose of clinging to various supports.

According to Miguel Covarrubias, a contemporary Mexican artist of note, natives of the Island of Bali like to eat dragonflies, which they catch in an unusual manner. Boys and girls wander among the rice fields waving long poles, the ends of which are smeared with a sticky saplike substance. The stick is held above the place where the dragonfly is hovering and when it alights on the end of the stick it becomes firmly stuck. Great numbers are caught in this way. The wings are broken off and then the bodies, mixed with spices and vegetables, are fried in coconut oil until crisp.

In Japan the dragonfly is a sign of victory and therefore has its place in the literature of that country. It is symbolically in evidence whenever past successes are being commemorated, or to arouse patriotic fervor for fresh encounters.

In Pennsylvania, in connection with notions about snakes there existed a belief that a species of dragonfly locally called "snake doctor," or "snake feeder," acted as a guard or acolyte to the serpents dwelling there. It supposedly warned snakes of approaching danger and also aided them in the acquisition of food. It was considered imprudent to kill such a "snake servant" because its master, the snake, would become angry and attack the slayer. A possible explanation of this linking of snakes and dragonflies may be the fact that both are commonly found inhabiting swampy areas.

In some rural sections the superstition exists that if a dragonfly alights on one's fishing line the fish will not bite. Another superstition is that it is bad luck to kill one. From the Isle of Wight comes the belief that the dragonfly possesses a very painful sting. There they have a legend respecting dragonflies and children who go fishing. According to this legend the dragonflies can distinguish good children from bad and when good boys go fishing the dragonflies will hover over the spot where the fish have settled under the banks, but when the bad boys go near the water they are almost sure to be stung.

Somewhat generally throughout the United States, it is also believed that dragonflies have stings, and in addition, that they will sew one's ears together. In New England they were thought to sew up various parts of the human body—lips, nostrils, eyelids or ears. In Iowa the superstition existed that the "devil's darning needle" would sew together the exposed fingers or toes of a person who went to sleep within its reach.

Of course dragonflies cannot sew up any part of the human body, and in spite of common and superstitious beliefs to the contrary—they do not sting. They *cannot* sting because they have no stinging apparatus. In fact, dragonflies may be regarded as beneficial to man, for in the larval stage they devour the larvae of mosquitoes and gnats and in the adult stage they devour many insect pests such as mosquitoes, gnats, and flies.

The wing expanse of the largest present-day dragonfly, *Megaloprepus caerulatus* of Central and South America, is over seven inches. This, however, is small indeed compared with the wingspread of the fossil dragonfly *Meganeura* that lived in the Pennsylvanian swamps during the Carboniferous period, some 250,000,000 years ago. *Meganeura* actually had a wingspread of over two feet! Dragonflies are believed to be the oldest known insects and they probably were the first animals to take to the air in flight.

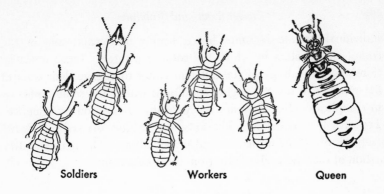

Soldiers   Workers   Queen

Chapter XII

Undercover Workers

The Termites

Termites are generally known as "white ants" but they are not ants, nor are they actually white.   In fact they are not even *distantly* related to ants, for scientists have now determined that termites evolved from roachlike ancestors.   As one can see at a glance from the outline illustrations of a termite and an ant, the termite may be readily distinguished from the ant by the absence of any constriction or "waist" where the abdomen joins the thorax.   Scientifically, termites are known as Isoptera, a word of Greek origin meaning "equal wings." It is likely that the selection of this name for the order was made on the basis of the observation that in the mature, sexual, winged adult forms, the front and hind wings are equal in shape, size, color, venation, and other characteristics.   Termites in Latin are called *termes,* a word also of Greek origin, meaning "woodworm."

Termites are social insects with instincts so highly developed that their organizations may be considered unique in the insect world. They are cooperative to the highest degree because within each nest it is the perpetuation of the colony that is the dominant factor—the

145

individual termite becomes but a readily replaceable cog in the complicated system by which the colony operates. These interrelationships—the ability of the different castes to change their ways of life in order to meet changing conditions within the same nest—are so complicated that they are not yet fully understood by scientists. Termites live in colonies like ants, but exhibit markedly different methods of colony formation and perpetuation. The nature and location of their nests also differ from those of the ants.

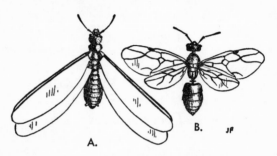

FIGURE 26. **The Difference Between an Ant and a Termite** A. A winged or adult termite showing wings of equal size, and a not too obvious constriction in the region where the thorax joins the abdomen.

B. A winged or adult ant showing wings that differ in size and in venation. Note the distinct constriction (known as the petiole) where the thorax joins the abdomen.

Termites live in darkness entirely shut off from the outside world and even from interconnection with other colonies of termites of the same species. They construct narrow passageways which serve to connect their source of food and their nest. Within these passageways and the nest itself, the temperature, the moisture, and the oxygen pressure are to some extent controlled by the manner in which they seal their cells against outside conditions. When they wish to extend their range of activity, they build additional passageways wherein they travel long distances to and from the nest, protected from daylight and from their enemies, and in a humid atmosphere. This humidity is a vital factor to termites because the outer covering, or cuticle, of their bodies is very delicate, even in the adult. Exposure to dry air, if only for a short period of time, may result in dehydration and death. The exception to this condition occurs at certain seasons of the year, at the time of the swarming flight when mature males and females develop wings and leave the protection of the nest in order to mate and form new colonies. At the time of the swarm, males and females fly out of the nest and courtship takes place during flight, but mating does not occur until they drop to the ground and break off their wings by striking themselves against some object. Then each pair of termites establishes a new colony, she as queen and he as king. If all goes well they may become the parents of a small brood within a few weeks. Their young are fed with droplets of food ejected from the mouths of the new king and queen, until the young are fully grown, after which individuals of the brood forage for their parents as well as for themselves. As the colony increases in the number of inhabitants they split into specialized castes, each caste performing a specific function.

In most species of termites the nest usually contains five castes—three fertile reproductive castes and two sterile castes. The fertile castes are capable of assisting the "royal pair" in increasing the nest population, but only under certain conditions. Under normal conditions it is the king and queen that populate the nest. The two sterile castes are the workers and the soldiers. The greater part of the duty of feeding the successive broods and of nest-building is performed by the workers. There may be two kinds of soldiers in tropical termite nests. One type has huge mandibles or pincers, and the other has a long nose through which it can project a gas attack. Each nest has one type or the other, but not both. It is the soldiers' task to protect the rest of the nest's inhabitants against enemies, such as ants and also some birds and mammals. A few species of ants are able to penetrate the walls of the termite nest and carry off their victims in great numbers. A few birds, such as some of the South American woodhewers may penetrate the superficial galleries with their elongated bills. But the most successful of the predatory mammals, against which termites have no protection, are the anteaters. The forefeet of the anteaters are ideally suited for breaking into the hard nests so that their long, sticky tongues may penetrate the nest cavities and gather up the insects. Other animals that habitually prey upon termites are the aardvark and the pangolin.

Subsequent to the founding of a new termite colony the increase of the nest population is fundamentally the function of the original king and queen. After the first brood has been reared the queen develops into what virtually amounts to an egg-laying machine, and she increases in size to about fifty times the size of the ordinary worker termite, sometimes attaining a length of three and one-half or more inches. She actually becomes so big, as a direct result of her greatly enlarged ovaries, that she loses the use of her legs for locomotion. The little king stays near her in the royal cell and their every need is taken care of by their numerous progeny. Observations of a certain African termite show that the queen lays eggs with almost clock-like regularity during a period of from six to fifteen years. She lays a tremendous number of eggs a day, and many millions during a full lifetime. The king cohabits with the queen for life, mating taking place at irregular intervals. Other reproductive castes in the nest become productive only in the event of the death of the king or queen, but if the death of either the king or queen occurs before the first brood matures, that is the end of that particular nest.

Termites may be considered insects of great economic importance since their chief food is cellulose which they obtain from dead wood. They are instrumental in clearing away stumps and fallen timber that would otherwise clog the forests and impede new growth. In addition to clearing away such debris they break down and reconvert these materials, thus indirectly enriching the soil. It is unfortunate that most people consider termites only as destructive insects, but this is principally because they attack wooden foundations of homes and in some cases, particularly in the tropics, undermine them to the point where they collapse. Naturally, termites are incapable of differentiating between house timbers and other dead wood since they and their ancestors have been "chewing" dead wood for *millions* of years. Curiously enough, some of the species that feed on wood have not the ability to digest it but must depend upon tiny one-celled organisms called Protozoa to do it for them. These Protozoa live in the intestines of the termites and by their chemical processes break down wood into a digestible form so that the termites can assimilate it. In the laboratory it has been demonstrated that by "sterilizing" termites of all Protozoa, they are rendered incapable of digesting wood and finally starve to death within two or three weeks. The "sterilization" has been accomplished in one of three ways: by keeping the temperature at about 97° F. for a day, by starvation, or by raising the oxygen pressure of the air. It was then demonstrated that if the termites were reinfected with these Protozoa they resumed their normal life and growth.

As a general rule termites are tropical insects and only a few species inhabit our northern climates. They live in various forms of nests, and often in the hearts of trees. The architecture of the nests they build may run to spires, monoliths, or huge mounds. In the tropics certain species of termites build structures that tower up to twenty feet.

Probably the most famous structures built by termites (*Hamitermes meridionalis*) are the "meridian" nests of northern Australia. In certain areas, usually in open or lightly-wooded country, these nests are numerous. They are long, narrow, and wedge-shaped, from three to twelve feet in height, about three and one-half feet through the middle at ground level, and they are famous because the narrow ends invariably face north and south and the sides face east

FIGURE 27. Man Standing Beside an Eight-Foot Meridian Nest.

and west. In the summer the termites seek the galleries at the base of the mound or go beneath the ground during the middle of the day. In the winter when some warmth is required, they use the eastern side in the morning and move to the western side in the afternoon. There has been much discussion concerning the unique construction of these meridian nests and the currently accepted theory is that they are built to expose the least surface to the sun's rays during the intense heat of tropical noon.

Another species of mound-building termite in Australia is *Nasutitermes exitosus,* which erects pillarlike structures reaching eighteen feet in height.   In order to confirm that each structure contains many millions of individuals, a sample nest only one and one-half feet high by four feet wide was opened.   The actual count from this small nest gave us the following interesting data:

Workers	1,560,000
Soldiers	200,000
Nymphs (immature termites)	40,000
Total population	1,800,000
Humidity—exceeding 95%	
Temperature—relatively high	

One of the oddest uses of termite nests is found among the head-hunters of the Amazon River in South America and is concerned with the rites surrounding the remarriage of a woman who has become a widow.   Besides observing other social taboos and conditions, she is required to pass through a purification ceremony before she is permitted to marry again.   The procedure calls for the woman to sit alongside a termite's nest with her head and the nest covered by a tent-like cloth.   The nest is then set on fire and she inhales the smoke until she is nearly suffocated.   This ceremony is believed to purify and free her from the taboo which became attached to her upon the death of her husband.

Although termites generally use vegetable substances for the construction of their nests, some species build nests of a clay which hardens to such a degree that it can be broken only with an axe. The early Spaniards in Brazil appropriated and carefully hollowed out such clay nests and then used them as ovens.   Another species of termites (found in Ceylon) makes nests from clay that is so pure and fine that the native goldsmiths use it for making crucibles and molds for their delicate metal castings, and also fashion their gods from it.

Strangely enough, the clay from certain termite nests is chewed by the natives in the lake region of central Africa in much the same manner as the Arabs of that region chew tobacco. Obviously it softens as it becomes mixed with saliva. The clay of which termite nests is constructed is nothing else, basically, but the dry and hardened termite feces. The Arabs, learning of this custom, tried it as a substitute for tobacco but suffered such attacks of severe nausea every time they attempted to chew it that they finally gave it up.

Termites themselves are also eaten, but their small size and the trouble of separating them from the debris of the nest make them difficult to prepare. A termite queen especially is considered a prize morsel. In the East Indies it is given to old men in the belief that it will effect rejuvenation and a strengthening of the back. Both the queen and the king are walled up in a "royal cell" the openings into which are too small to allow either of the royal pair to get out, but large enough to permit the entry and exit of the workers who tend them. However, in spite of a termite queen's trapped quarters she is a very difficult insect to get at since she lies deep within the heart of a nest containing millions of inhabitants, and searching for her calls for both skill and experience.

Members of the Bantu tribe of South Africa eagerly collect swarming termites by placing pails of water under the nest opening, into which many of the insects fall and drown as they emerge from the nest. These are used for food, and here is a rare recipe for "Termites à la Bantu":

> 1 pint termites
> 1 tablespoon vegetable oil (ground or palm nut)
> ½ teaspoon salt, if available.

Remove termite wings. Spread on flat stone in sun to dry. Smear pan or stone with oil and spread dried termites upon it. Toast over hot coals until almost crisp. Sprinkle with salt. Eat like popcorn immediately or store for future use—they can be stored for months!

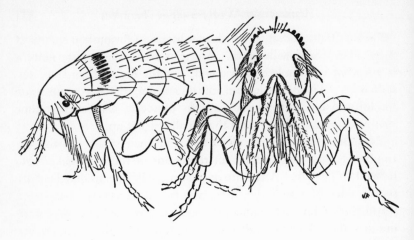

Chapter XIII

Pests of Pets and People

The Fleas

It is often said that no matter how small an animal is there is always a smaller animal to feed upon it. Even fleas, which are parasitic in nature, are themselves infested with smaller parasites. To show their prevalence the following rhyme is often quoted:

Great fleas have little fleas upon their backs to bite 'em.
And little fleas have lesser fleas, and so *ad infinitum.*
And the great fleas themselves, in turn, have greater fleas to go on;
While these again have greater still, and greater still, and so on.

Fleas are adapted for a parasitic way of life and the better known species are those normally associated with rats and other rodents, dogs, cats, and human beings. They have been grouped together under the Order Siphonaptera. The word Siphonaptera refers to the form of the flea's siphon or tubelike mouthparts, and to the absence of wings at any stage of development (*Siphon* = siphon; *aptera* = wingless).

152

Fleas scatter their eggs on the floors where flea-infested animals sleep. The larvae are creamy-white, slender, hairy, wormlike creatures that feed upon loose hairs and skin-scales which have fallen from animals and which have accumulated in crevices. These larvae spin cocoons within which the pupal stage is passed, and by the time they have reached the adult stage they have developed long, sharp, sucking beaks with which they puncture the skin and suck blood. Both male and female fleas must feed on blood for without it they cannot live. It is at this stage that they become known to us, for not until then are they capable of annoying us and our household pets. And since a single flea will bite many times, it often seems as if a house were overrun with them when, in reality, only a few are present.

The body of the adult flea is ideally suited for gliding through the narrow spaces between the hairs of its host, being oval and greatly compressed laterally, and since the body-covering is also smooth and firm it escapes easily when an attempt is made to catch it either between the fingers of man or between the teeth of lower mammals. Once out of the clutch of an enemy, the flea quickly leaps away. It is this unusual power of leaping that enables it to transfer readily from mammal to mammal. The human flea has been known to leap for a distance of thirteen inches, and to a height of seven and three-quarter inches. An equivalent leap for a man would carry him 275 feet up into the air and 450 feet horizontally!

Although certain species of fleas prefer to live upon specific mammals they are not necessarily restricted to their preferred hosts. For instance, both dog fleas and cat fleas frequently attack man—but only in the absence of their preferred hosts. For example, if a house containing flea-infested pets such as cats or dogs were vacated for a period of several weeks, the larvae, in the course of natural development, would become adult fleas. Then, in the absence of their preferred hosts (either cats or dogs in this case) their hunger would drive them to attack any person entering the house. The human body is *not* the normal or preferred host for fleas ordinarily associated with lower mammals.

The human body *is* the normal host for the human flea, *Pulex irritans*, which, as the name implies, irritates. The name *Pulex* was

given to the human flea by the Romans because of their mistaken belief that fleas originated from pulvis, or dirt. Thomas Moffett had the
same opinion. He thought that fleas were produced from the dust,
especially when moistened with urine, and that the smallest ones developed from putrid matter. A contemporary idea was that they
were produced from the moistened "humors" (excretions from skin)
among the hairs of dogs. *Pulex irritans* is not normally associated with
transmitting disease to human beings.

The insect that is guilty of transmitting bubonic plague is *Xenopsylla
cheopis*, the flea associated with rats. Originally it was native to the
Nile Valley region of Africa but in the course of world-wide trade it
has spread with its host, which is the domestic rat, to all parts of the
world.

In regions where living space is crowded and unsanitary conditions
prevail, the rat population is likely to be high. As the rat population
increases, fleas become very numerous because of the short period of
time it takes them to develop from the egg to the adult stage. Under
such conditions rat fleas will readily feed upon human beings. Their
bites are annoying, but aside from the irritation they cause they are
not dangerous *except* in areas where the fleas are infected with bubonic
plague. The usual manner in which bubonic plague, or the "black
plague" as it has been known throughout history, is transmitted to
man is by means of the bite of a plague-infected rat flea. The disease
organism causing plague is *Pasteurella pestis*, a tiny one-celled bacillus.
Once bitten by a plague-infected flea, the rat serves as a reservoir of
infection and harbors *Pasteurella pestis* until it dies. But until death
does overtake the rat, every flea that feeds upon it imbibes plague
organisms in its meal of blood and thus becomes a carrier of bubonic
plague. Once the plague organisms are in the body of a flea they
multiply rapidly in the region of the flea's crop. The multiplication
is so great that the flea soon becomes incapable of swallowing and
consequently is doomed to death by starvation. Meanwhile, being
hungry, the flea constantly tries to feed. In preparation for the
insertion of the beak into the flesh of a man or other mammal, a flea
first lubricates the puncture site with its regurgitated saliva. Therefore, since it is in the saliva of an infected flea that the plague organisms

are contained, in this manner baccilli are introduced into the blood-stream.

Bubonic plague is a disease that is characterized by the formation of "buboes" (swellings) in the regions of the neck, groin, or armpits. It has been the scourge of mankind since early days and probably has been the cause of deaths far in excess of any loss of life due to warfare. History tells us of several plagues that raged unchecked for many years. The first recorded plague epidemic occurred in the time of Justinian in the sixth century, starting in Egypt in 542 A.D., and spreading to Constantinople. This epidemic lasted between fifty and sixty years and has been estimated to have claimed at least one hundred million victims. Another epidemic swept Europe in the fourteenth century and historians note that the "Black Death" took a toll of about twenty-five million lives, or one-quarter of the population of Europe. London's great plague epidemic (1664–1666) is said to have killed seventy thousand persons.

Insects were being recognized as disease transmitters as early as the sixteenth century but the belief was that plague was transmitted *by flies* from those who were ill or dead to those who were well. The knowledge of the manner in which this disease was actually spread was not forthcoming until about 1894. Since then we have come to under-stand that the destruction of rats is the most important means of eradicating bubonic plague and thus preventing epidemics from deci-mating entire areas of population. While plague is primarily a dis-ease of rats, another rodent found guilty of harboring the plague bacillus is the ground squirrel of California. This squirrel has been the cause of minor outbreaks of bubonic plague in some of our western states.

In Europe during the sixteenth century well-born ladies wore "flea-furs" around their shoulders in order to attract and trap fleas. And while it is well known that fleas were also common in eastern countries (and still are), it is surprising to learn that in this country in Missouri, the early American explorers, Clark and Lewis, found them more tormenting than all other discomforts. They reported that the prevalence of

FIGURE 28. Lady Wearing Flea-Fur Neck-piece.

fleas sometimes compelled the inhabitants to shift their living quarters.

The fox, which is fabled for his cleverness, is credited with having devised an ingenious method of ridding himself of fleas. As early as 1634, Thomas Moffett records an interesting account of how a fox rid himself of fleas. The fox was seen gathering up bits of hair adhering to thorn and briar bushes. He rolled these into a compact mass and held one end of this mass firmly between his front teeth while he slowly waded into a cold river—*backwards*. In this manner he gradually submerged himself until just his snout and the mass of hair was above the level of the water. The fleas, in order to get away from the slowly rising water, by gradual leaps all congregated in the mass of hair that the fox so cleverly held in his teeth all this while. The fox barked and spat out the flea-laden hair, and then swam back to land.

Considering the great age of Moffett's story, it is interesting to have found, in the August 5th, 1944 issue of the *Saturday Evening Post*, what amounts to a verification of this ingenious method of getting rid of fleas. The author of the article evidently was not familiar with the incident reported over three hundred years before because he thought he was making a new contribution to science on the intelligence of animals. The modern version is reported to have taken place in southern Illinois and the story in its details so closely parallels the one published in 1634 that the similarity is startling. The fox in this story collected wool that festooned the barbed wire fence where sheep had brushed against it. He continued until his mouth was full and then trotted off to a nearby pond. At the edge, the wily fox turned around and slowly backed into the water. At last he was entirely submerged except for the tip of his nose and the bunch of wool sticking out of his mouth. The man then noticed that the fox suddenly leaped from the water, dropped the wool, and dashed away. Being curious, he walked down to the pond, picked up the wool, and found it to be alive with fleas. It seems that this information was not startling to a friend to whom he told the story because his friend retaliated with a story about a pet raccoon who rid himself of fleas in a similar manner.

From time to time it is affirmed that asses are never troubled with fleas, and the only reason one finds recorded to account for this strange belief is that "Christ rode upon the back of one of these animals." The inference in these affirmations seems to be that since it was this beast that carried Christ, it was freed of these insect tormentors. However, since entomologists have collected fleas from these animals, it would seem that this belief is unfounded.

It is sometimes claimed that fleas have been "trained" to perform in Flea Circuses. Apparently, once a flea has painstakingly been made to perform a certain act repeatedly, the act becomes such a firmly established conditioned reflex that the flea is incapable of breaking away from it.

Fleas were the original objects on which the simple microscope was turned in the Middle Ages. In fact, these instruments were commonly known as "flea glasses" (vitrea pulicaria). Several hundred years elapsed before the novelty of these magnifiers wore off and scientists began serious investigation with compound microscopes.

MISCELLANEOUS

PROVERBS:

"A flea on your hand, a letter from the country."
"Nothing should be done in a hurry except catching fleas."
"That's a valiant flea that dare eat his breakfast on the lip of a lion."
"The fatter the flea, the leaner the dog."
"A bag of fleas is easier to keep watch over than a woman."
"He who sleeps well does not feel the fleas."
"One flea cannot raise a coverlet."
"One flea does not hinder sleep."
"Dogs have fleas in order to keep them from thinking about being dogs."
"Flea-luggit." [Scottish—to be unsettled or confused.]

GENERAL:

"To send one away with a flea in his ear" is an old English phrase meaning to dismiss one with a rebuke.
The "little sable beast" if much thirsting after blood, augurs rain.

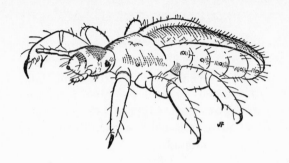

Chapter XIV

Intimate Intruders

The Lice

The word "louse" is often applied to insects which are not true lice, such as the book louse, the plant louse (the aphid), the bark louse (the scale insect), and the bee louse (which is a fly). As a matter of fact, the term "louse" is often applied to animals that are not even insects, such as the wood louse (the sow bug or pill bug), and the fish louse. In this chapter we shall concern ourselves only with the true "blood-sucking" lice in this Order (Anoplura)—the lice that are parasitic on mammals—because they are the ones that may affect human beings.

Lice are small insects, somewhat flattened in form, and like the fleas are blood-sucking parasites that do not at any time possess wings. Their mouthparts are also of the piercing-sucking type. When the beak of a louse is not in use it is completely withdrawn into the head so that all one can usually see externally, through a microscope, is a fringe of minute teeth at the foremost part of the head. Lice have developed strong claws, situated at the end of the last joint of each of their six legs, which clasp hairs firmly, thus enabling them to maintain a hold on active animals. These claws are also used to hold on to

158

seams of clothing, usually the inside seams, in order to take advantage of human body warmth.

The female louse "cements" her eggs, commonly called "nits," to the inner seams of woolen clothing and to the hairs of man or other mammals. One female may lay an average of ten eggs a day for a period of from twenty to thirty days. The young become active as soon as they hatch, proceeding to suck blood with their unique mouthparts. The young resemble the adults in shape and form from the moment they hatch.

Lice are highly specialized insects normally found on their preferred animal hosts. In other words, animal lice will usually be found only on certain animal hosts, while human body lice prefer and are invariably found on human beings. Lice are also very sensitive to what has been aptly called the climatic condition of the skin—its temperature and humidity—and prefer a temperature slightly lower than that of the body, which they ordinarily find by clinging to seams of clothing next to the body or to the hairs of mammals. If the body has a high fever, or if the body cools, as when death takes place, the lice will leave and seek another host.

The species of lice infesting man are considered to be three in number—the head louse, the body louse, and the pubic or "crab" louse. They vary in color from white to brown. When young and recently fed, the blood meal can be seen through the skin and they appear to be bright red. In soldier vocabulary they are then known as "red backs." As digestion takes place the blood becomes darker. They are then called "black backs" or "gray backs." Because of these changes in coloration the same lice are often mistaken for different species. In soldier's slang in World War I all body lice were known as "cooties," but World War II made that term obsolete—the modern version is "motorized dandruff!"

Body lice and head lice can transfer from one person to another upon contact, and sitting next to an infested person in a train is a close enough contact for this transfer to take place. Normally, lice are rather slow-moving insects, but they are capable of moving with sufficient speed to give weight to the old saying: "You can't catch a louse with one finger."

Infestations of lice have been known since ancient times in all parts of the world. Besides being transmitters of typhus fever, lice also carry relapsing fever and trench fever from one person to another. The transmission of typhus from a louse to a human victim is not accomplished by means of mouthparts, as usually occurs with other disease-transmitting insects. Typhus is caused by minute organisms known as Rickettsia which develop in the intestinal tract and are contained in the fecal matter of typhus-infected lice. These microorganisms gain entrance into the human body when the fecal matter harboring Rickettsia is rubbed into small cuts or skin abrasions, and are the disease-producing organisms actually responsible for typhus fever. Just the crushing of a single typhus-infected louse on broken skin will cause typhus. Recently it has been established that in a contaminated area where there is much dust and dirt, one can also become infected with typhus by rubbing the contaminated dust or dirt into the eyes, or by merely inhaling it.

While typhus is not necessarily fatal, it is exceedingly debilitating, and very often for long periods of time. It occurs in epidemic proportions when there is famine, filth, privation, overcrowding, in the slums of large cities, among primitive tribes, and in concentration camps of refugees or prisoners of war. Under such conditions as these, human resistance is low and the death rate is high.

Typhus epidemics are usually associated with wars. In early literature typhus fever was recorded as brig fever, ship fever, gaol fever, and spotted fever—the spotted condition of the body being one of the symptoms. The term typhus, from the Greek word *typhos* meaning "smoke," refers to the coma or stupor which is another symptom of this fever. Hippocrates first described these symptoms in 460 B.C., although the name "typhus fever" was not used until the eighteenth century.

History records that when the armies of Ferdinand and Isabella besieged Granada in the fifteenth century, about 15,000 soldiers died of typhus—more than six times the number killed in action. Typhus almost wiped out a French army besieging Naples in the sixteenth century when, out of an army of 25,000 men, 21,000 died of this disease. It played havoc with Napoleon's army on its disastrous retreat from

Moscow.   One of the largest epidemics of the eighteenth century occurred among British seamen fighting in the Revolutionary War.
More than one-quarter of a million persons are said to have died of the
disease in Germany from 1813 to 1814, and in Russia between 1919
and 1922 no less than 10,000,000 cases of typhus occurred in an area
having a population of 120,000,000 people, 3,000,000 of whom died.

That louse-born typhus should have been
so prevalent in the past reveals a good deal
about the unsanitary conditions under which
our ancestors lived—that they were "lousy"
was a condition of the time accepted as being
unavoidable.   In fact, one of the reasons why
gentlemen shaved their heads and wore wigs
a few hundred years ago was the difficulty
they had in keeping their own hair free from
lice.   And as for the ladies of the court, it
was quite fashionable for them to carry long
currycombs for scratching their backs.   Aside
from such references in the literature, the
"scratching stick" which is a heritage from
those times is mute evidence of the fact that
it was no shame to be lousy.   These were
thin sticks about a foot in length, at one end

**FIGURE   29.   Lady
Dressed in the Height of
Fashion—Complete with
Scratching Stick!**

of which a small hand was carved with fingers bent in the scratching
position.   It was a convenient implement to slip under the garments
to alleviate itching in places which would otherwise have been inac-
cessible, for in those days ladies had garments sewed right on them
which were not removed every night.   Until comparatively recent
times Newfoundlanders actually considered it an indication of "good
health" for a person to be lousy.

At Hardenburg, Sweden, about a century ago, there existed an
unusual method of choosing a Burgomaster.   All the men who were
eligible and aspired to the position sat around a table, bending low so
that their beards rested upon it.   A louse was then placed in the
center of the table and the one in whose beard the insect first took
cover was designated the Burgomaster for the forthcoming year.

FIGURE 30.

In medieval times morals and learning were dominated by holy men who, zealously censuring world luxuries, sanctioned dirt and vermin as a sign of lack of self-indulgence. That *they* did not kill lice was accepted as a manifestation of their humility and proof that they did not consider themselves superior to any living thing—not even to a louse. A translation depicting such a condition was made from the Latin account of the murder of Archbishop Thomas à Becket in 1170 A.D. The vivid description follows: "and the next day, after some debate, it was decided to remove the clothing in preparation for burial. The dead Archbishop was clad in an extraordinary accumulation of garments. Outermost there was a large brown mantle; next, a white surplice; underneath this, a fur coat of lamb's wool; then a woolen pelisse; then another woolen pelisse; below this, the black cowled robe of the Benedictine Order; then, a shirt; and finally, next to the body, a tightly-fitting suit of coarse haircloth covered on the outside with linen, the first of its kind seen in England. The innumerable vermin which had infested the dead prelate were stimulated to such activity by the cold, that this haircloth garment, in the words of a chronicler, 'boiled over with them like water in a simmering cauldron, and the onlookers burst into alternate fits of weeping and laughter, between the sorrow of having lost such a head, and the joy of having found such a saint!' "

From the time of the Pharaohs the idea has prevailed that lice were produced from dirt: "And there were lice upon man, and upon beast; all the dust of the earth became lice throughout the land of Egypt."

During the Boer War, after a damp or rainy night, the men would spread their blankets in the sun to dry. The heat of the sun would make the lice move about so that what had appeared to be a clean, uninfested blanket actually became alive with lice. The soldiers believed it was contact with the ground that caused this and therefore these insects were often called "ground lice." This association of "dirt" and "lice" through the ages is responsible for the still existing belief that only dirty people become lousy. For that reason many a clean person who acquired lice in a train or crowded subway has suffered his discomforting secret in silence. However, the fact is that lice beget lice. They are not generated by dirty conditions. No matter how unclean a person may be, he cannot become infested with lice unless he comes in contact with someone who is harboring them.

Before the First World War the head louse was the species with which the average person was familiar. Even in the best regulated schools children frequently became infested with them, but the number of lice diminished rapidly as bobbed hair increased in popularity. And as the frequent changing of underclothing became a more pronounced habit, body lice also became scarcer. Today human lice are things of the past except where existing conditions combine overcrowding, ill-housing, and lack of sufficient sanitation.

While the mention of lice in polite society is now frowned upon, the Ozarker continues to take them in his stride and provides a place for them in his scheme of things. He believes that the *first* louse found upon a child's head should be cracked—on a tin cup if his child is to become a dancer, on a songbook if his child is to become a singer, and on a Bible if his child is to become a reader and a speaker of the truth; but the first louse should never be killed on the child's head for fear that the child may grow up to be a simpleton! A somewhat similar superstition existed among the Pennsylvania Germans. They believed that if a louse was placed on the child's head before the child was nine days old, and the child then carried to the upper story of the house, he would become imbued with "lofty" thoughts later in life.

What probably is the prize medical use of sow or hog lice is recorded by Dr. Brickell: "The whole insect is thin and of volatile parts, digesting, cleaning, opening and a great dissolver of all tartarous matter, therefore good in all obstructions, jaundice, colic, King's Evil [tuberculosis], old sordid and rebellious ulcers, convulsions, stone and gravel, rickets in children, dimness of sight, French Pax, and many other stubborn and lingering disorders."

Another unusual description of the use of hog lice is recorded in an English book on pharmacy printed in London in 1741. The formula is called *Vinum Millepedum*, or Hog Lice Wine, and is prepared as follows: "Take hog lice, half a pound, put them alive in two pounds of port wine, and after some days' infusion strain and press out very hard; then put in saffron (two drachms), salt of steel (one drachm), and salt of amber (two scruples), and after 3–4 days strain and filter for use." This concoction was prescribed as "an admirable medicine against the jaundice, dropsy or any cachetic habit. It greatly deterges all the viscera and throws off a great deal of superfluous poison by urine. It may be given twice a day, two ounces at a time."

Dreaming of lice (depending upon the locality) indicates a variety of things to the superstitious-minded. In Newfoundland it is a sign of enemies or a sign of death. In Alabama it is a sign of coming wealth. In Louisiana it may be either a sign of coming wealth or a sign of approaching illness, either to the dreamer or to the dreamer's family. In the Bahamas, where Voodooism is practiced, we find a more practical superstition: if a louse is thrown into a sail it will cause a wind.

In both literature and speech the use of the word "louse" applied to a human being has always signified something uncomplimentary, derogatory, or just downright contemptible. At the very least, it is a term of reproach. The word has also been used as the subject of many a ribald joke. A classic example is that which involved Theodore Hook, a gentleman (?) who, after being turned out of the house of the Third Countess of Holland (by the Countess herself, no less!), took his pen in hand and wrote:

> My Ladyship said when I called at her house,
> She didn't esteem me three slips of a louse;
> But I freely forgave what the dear creature said,
> For women will talk of what runs in their head.

Chapter XV

Progress–Science and Insects

Although insects have been on the earth for many millions of years, and their importance in man's efforts to produce food and to live in comfort has been recognized since the dawn of history, the scientific study of them, called Entomology, is relatively new. During the few centuries that insects have been under scrutiny, endless facts about their evolution, their life histories, and their place in the balance of nature have been brought to light. While many are found to be beneficial and others innocuous, human welfare demands that some be rigidly kept at a minimum. In this final chapter, to show how vitally insects have come to affect man's everyday life, the spotlight will be swung from their earliest beginnings to the opportunities which science offers today for their study and effective control.

It is possible that insects had their origin sometime during the early part of the Paleozoic era, some 500 millions of years ago. Definite impressions of ancient insects have been discovered in rock strata of the Devonian period, which began about 325 million years ago. These earliest known insect forms were wingless. In Scotland, actual fragments of some small wingless insects have been recovered in the flint-like rock (chert) which dates from this era.

165

In the Carboniferous (coal-bearing) period, which began about 280 million years ago, the fossil record shows that insect wing venation and body parts were already well developed. Such nonflowering, primitive plants as ferns and mosses flourished then, and the coal beds of today were formed from the vast deposits of vegetable matter laid down at that time. Among these newly developing plant forms, insects increased in size and numbers. Some dragonfly-like insects acquired a wing spread of two and one-half feet! It was from these forms that the cockroach-type of insect evolved, and became so abundant that this time in earth history is often called the "Age of Cockroaches."

Then in the Permian period, some 220 million years ago, great climatic changes took place. The moist and warm climate which had prevailed gave way to one of widespread cold and aridity. With the cooling of the climate, the large forms of insects gave rise to countless numbers of smaller-sized species, and the first representatives of many of our modern orders of insects appeared.

During the Jurassic period, about 150 million years ago, the climate moderated and again insects increased in size and numbers. By the beginning of the Cretaceous period, approximately 20 million years later, the flowering plants had become established in a complementary development of insect-pollinated plants and pollen-and-nectar-feeding insects.

The insects of today are thus the result of evolutionary forces correlated in great part with climatic conditions of the past. Changes in climate will probably be an equally important factor in modifying the insects of the future ages. But the fact remains that insects have been able to survive and reproduce new generations for hundreds of millions of years and will, in all likelihood, continue to survive. In spite of man's attempts to exterminate certain species, none has ever disappeared from the earth because of his activities.

Although insects have been abundant since the late Paleozoic age, they are comparatively rare as fossils because existing conditions did not insure adequate preservation. For example, no insects are known to inhabit salt water, although a few species do live in brackish water. Therefore, insect remains are not found in the sedimentary rocks of marine origin formed when the seas covered what is now dry land.

Also, insects are not well adapted for fossilization, since the chitin which is such an integral part of any insect is to some extent soluble in water. Most of the known insect fossils have been found in accumulations of vegetable matter, such as coal, peat, and lignite, or in fresh-water basins where the insects were probably drowned and rapidly embedded.

Insects in rich variety also have been found in Baltic amber, the fossilized resin of coniferous trees that grew in northern Europe during the Tertiary period, which started some 75 million years ago and ended 35 million later. As this resinous substance exuded, it entangled and enveloped the insect, a process that may be observed occurring today. Another location where fossil insects have been found in recent years is in the famous La Brea tar pits of southern California. Here many insect fragments and even entire insects have been recovered. Carefully cleaned of the embedding tar, these have then been examined by specialists, principally at the Los Angeles County Museum.

Scientific study of insects began with Aristotle. He included in a single class which he called "Entoma" all the true insects, as well as the spiders (arachnids), and the millipedes and centipedes (myriapoda). Little progress was made for several hundred years after his work. Most of the people who took up the subject were primarily concerned with collecting as many species as possible. Entomology as a formal study is a relatively recent science. Taxonomy, that branch which deals with naming and classification, did not progress much until the early part of the last century. Scientists then provided many needed descriptions of species and catalogues listing scientific names.

While most of the early students assembled collections of adult insect specimens, others turned their energies to studying life histories. In the United States this study first began to assume the status of a profession after the Civil War. It was given impetus then by the Morrill Act of 1862, which was responsible for the establishment of state agricultural colleges in this country. This was the first step in the gradual decline of the free-lance amateur entomologist and in the rise of the professionally trained one, whose knowledge could be used to help farmers.

Usually credited with being the first teacher of entomology in America is Dr. H. A. Hagen (about 1871), although a man by the name of Harris, a Harvard librarian, is said to have had a private class in the subject in 1831. Dr. L. O. Howard (until his death in 1950, one of the foremost American entomologists) stated that Hagen had been brought over to Harvard from Germany by Agassiz in 1870 for the express purpose of teaching the subject. Before that time the instructor in entomology was also a teacher of natural history, which included botany, zoology, and geology.

As the number of professionally trained entomologists grew, the science added to its own vocabulary. At present the full understanding of its extensive literature requires knowledge of other specialized subjects, too. The modern entomologist now calls to his aid the discoveries made in other fields of science and in return passes on the results of his work for the benefit of medicine, agriculture, and industry.

This is the present-day procedure. Economic or applied entomology—the aspect of insect study concerned with human affairs—was unknown at the beginning of the eighteenth century. Some of the contemporary recommendations for insect control, such as salt, lime, alcohol, lampblack, and cayenne pepper, are recognized today as of little or no insecticidal value. In 1760 George Washington was experimenting with various substances in an effort to reduce the number of Hessian flies.

The science of insect control started to assume importance about 1800, and a brief chronology in connection with disease control will show its development. In 1807 copper salts were sprayed against fungus diseases; in 1821 sulphur was used to combat peach mildew; in 1860 Paris green was one of the first arsenicals employed against the Colorado potato beetle; in 1886 lime sulphur was used as a stock dip against external insect parasites. In 1892 arsenicals of lead were used against the gypsy moth; this still remains a standard spray against insects with chewing mouthparts, more than three million pounds being used annually.

A shift in emphasis to biological methods, or, as they were then termed, "natural" methods of control, took place about the turn of this century. This change had an economic and social basis. From

1789 to 1820, there were 259,127 alien arrivals in the United States; but from June 30, 1901 to June 30, 1910 mass migrations settled 9,771,512 persons upon our shores. A large percentage of these newcomers were agriculturally minded, and since there was need for farm crops many of them engaged in farming as a vocation. As great areas of trees were cleared and the ground tilled, the problem of insect pests became more acute, and profitable farm production became more and more dependent on preventing losses caused by insects. This was one of the reasons why biological methods gained momentum. "Set an insect to catch an insect" may be said to be the essence of biological control. To state it in another way, research was centered on predators or parasites that might effectively keep pests in check. If this could be accomplished, it would be an obvious boon to farmers.

In the last two decades many large chemical manufacturers have entered the field of entomology. Some are developing new compounds that are poisonous to insects, some are seeking to improve already established insecticides. This movement has necessitated research into fundamental problems of insect life, especially in biochemistry and physiology, as a means of making possible further advances in the methods of insect control. Already discoveries in these new fields have proved of great value, for they are providing the answers to many puzzles of insect physiology in relation to insecticidal action.

The problems faced by these scientists have a long and world-wide history. America's European settlers brought with them many fruits and grains, and they also unwittingly introduced at least a third of the injurious insects with which we are confronted today. The codling moth made its appearance in this way and has since developed into a most serious pest, particularly of apples, and will probably be a major problem for years to come. The Hessian fly (pest of wheat), the oystershell scale (pest of fruit and ornamental trees), and the clothes moth were also brought into the United States and established here as early as the eighteenth century.

Very often insects which become serious pests in America are not particularly destructive in their native surroundings. One reason is that when an insect is introduced to another country it finds none of the normal enemies which had served to keep it in check. Also, it often adapts its feeding habits to the food available in the new environment, and this habit may result in great damage to crops of economic importance. The majority of insect pests in the United States have been introduced through the eastern seaports—Boston, New York, and Philadelphia. Others, such as the San José scale (a pest of fruit and ornamental trees), have arrived through western ports from some of the Pacific Islands. Some have come to us across the Mexican border, as did the sugar cane borer and the cotton boll weevil.

The common cabbage butterfly, a pest of plants belonging to the cabbage family, originally entered the United States from Quebec around 1860 and succeeded in crossing the continent in twenty-six years. On the other hand, the Colorado potato beetle is native to the Rocky Mountains where it originally fed upon a plant known as buffalo bur. This beetle has a unique history. As the early settlers migrated westward and planted potatoes, the beetles forsook the hardy buffalo bur in preference for the cultivated potato plants. Using the cultivated land plots as stepping stones they gradually moved eastward, crossing the United States in approximately fifteen years.

Some insect pests, such as the gypsy moth, purposely introduced into this country for experimental purposes, have spread by accident. In an attempt to breed better silkworms, Monsieur Leopold Trouvélot, a French astronomer and naturalist who lived in Medford, Massachusetts, in 1868, had eggs of the gypsy moth sent to him from Europe with the idea of interbreeding silkworm moths with gypsy moths. When the eggs arrived and had hatched he reared the caterpillars on shrubs in his garden within a carefully screened enclosure. The actual experiment proved a dismal failure and all would have been well had it ended at this point, but a sudden windstorm ripped away the protective screening and the caterpillars were thus accidentally released. Monsieur Trouvélot was alarmed because he knew that the escaped insects were a potential source of danger in this country, in spite of the fact that they were quite common and not a pest in their native habitat. He reported the accident immediately, but an uninterested community did not take action. The caterpillars of these gypsy moths eat the leaves of almost any broad-leaved tree, of certain plants that are not trees, especially cranberries, and the older caterpillars even feed on evergreens. After about ten years, when they started to swarm in noticeable numbers, it became apparent that the few escaped insects had acclimated themselves in the area. By 1890, the citizens were asking for state action against this pest. Then for the next ten years control work restricted the damage to an area of about 400 square miles. In 1900, despite strong objections from entomologists, appropriations were curtailed in a false economy move. Only a few years were needed to show the folly of this action, for by 1904 over 4,000 square miles were infested, including parts of Maine, New Hampshire, Rhode Island, and Massachusetts. At present the moths are checked but not controlled, and constant vigilance is maintained to prevent future outbreaks resulting in the defoliation of trees.

The locust probably is man's most ancient insect enemy, and one of the most persistent. As recently as 1952 locusts swarmed in French Somaliland, Eritrea, the Sudan, Aden, Yemen, Saudi Arabia, Oman, Kuwait, Jordan, Egypt, Israel, Syria, Iraq, Iran, and Pakistan. The infestations began in the spring of that year in a limited area of East Africa, but the insects spread with such rapidity that they threatened to cause one of the worst plagues of desert locusts seen in a hundred years. Shadowed with destruction were the cotton and grain of the Nile Delta on the one side and the rice fields of India on the other, and to combat this infestation effectively, international action was considered necessary. Now a war against these insects is going on, backed by many nations through the United Nations' Food and Agricultural Organization and also by our own Point Four Program of aid to undeveloped foreign regions. The locusts have been, and still are being, subjected to relentless air-ground attacks with concentrated doses of insecticides, using the latest methods and equipment.

Eventually such locust swarms disperse and enter a solitary phase. No one knows exactly what causes their disappearance but many years pass in which not a single locust is seen in areas previously attacked. At the outset of a migration, however, some insects seem to remain in the breeding grounds to begin a new cycle at a later time. Pods containing 25 to 100 eggs are laid by the females. These hatch in two to three weeks and the young nymphs develop rapidly, molting about five or six times before reaching adulthood. Their entire life is believed to extend for a period of five to six months, so that one generation begins a migration and successive generations complete it.

These locust cycles remain one of the mysteries of science. The irregularity of the intervals between locust outbreaks—periodicity— has long attracted attention and various explanations have been advanced to account for it. There seems to be very little doubt that periodicity is the result of certain environmental influences which act either directly or indirectly upon the insects. A thorough study of each locust species, in relation to fluctuations in external conditions over a period of years, would be the most profitable way of arriving at a real understanding of the factors which regulate outbreaks of the insects.

Some studies of this kind have been made. For example, Argentine investigators have related locust migrations to sunspots, claiming that locusts throughout the world reach a migratory phase in years when the fewest sunspots are observed. As evidence, they cite decreased sunspots in 1923–26, 1934–36, and 1946–47. These were all years when migrations took place.

In 1921 Uvarov advanced as a working hypothesis what is now known as the phase theory of locusts. Later observations, conducted in both the laboratory and the field by other workers, have so fully strengthened its main points that the phase theory is regarded today as an established biological occurrence. This theory is based upon the fact that the migratory species of true locusts (Acrididae) are polymorphic—that is, they occur in several distinct forms. Instead of being constant in all their characteristics, they are capable of developing obvious differences in color, structure, and behavior. According to the studies, migratory locusts exist in three readily changeable biological phases. In the first phase (solitary), they are scattered and do not concentrate in large groups. The second phase (transitional), finds them neither solitary nor massed. In the third or final phase (gregarious), the locusts gather in great numbers. The solitary phase may have an enormous area of distribution, whereas the gregarious phase occurs only in certain regions. Migratory species are often so strikingly distinct, in the first and last phase, that in the past locusts of one species have been mistaken for two separate species.

The transition from the nonswarming phase is caused by certain meteorological conditions which set in motion a complicated chain re-action in the biology of the locust. This follows a pattern: the biological changes culminate in the swarming phase, the swarming brings about a crisis, which in turn is followed by a decline that again results in a solitary phase. The solitary phase completes the cycle, which remains static until such time as meteorological conditions again initiate a repetition of the cycle.

Although the phase theory is still highly tentative in regard to fundamental causes, it can be utilized in two alternate methods of insect-control procedure: (1) the possibility that the mass transformation of locusts in the gregarious phase may be forestalled, and (2) the possibility of altering the character of the breeding grounds, thus rendering them less potent sources of invasion of other lands. But the ultimate solution has not yet been found.

While the menace of locust swarms is now being fought with a new American insecticide known as Aldrin, application of artificial control measures still remains hopelessly inadequate against great invasions. Being remedial in its effect, the prompt application of insecticides may alleviate a pressing problem, but the menace of subsequent swarms is left unaffected. And who knows how the locusts will react with newer generations? Will they develop resistant strains that can no longer be killed by chemicals? In other words, the solution of the problem lies not in remedial efforts but in arriving at a complete understanding of the biology of the locust. Only the research of the future can give us the answer to this most ancient of insect perils.

Insects may be studied today under many different headings: morphology and systematics—which concern the structure and orderly classification of existing species of insects; phylogeny—the study of the ancestors of insects, their near-relatives, and the relationship that exists betweeen them; genetics—the study of heredity of the insects; embryology—the history of the individual insect; ecology—the study of environment of the species and the interrelationships of insects, including the social life of the insects and their relationships with plants and animals and their economic relationship to man. These are some of the major divisions under which the study of insects is now carried on.

On the other hand, the general study of insecticidal action may be pursued at three levels: (1) the study of the uptake of the insecticides from the environment; (2) the study of the passage of insecticides through the protective coverings of the insect or its egg; and (3) the study of the effect of intervention of insecticidal poisons on the metabolism of insects. Knowledge of the structures of the cuticle of the insect and of the eggshell explains to some extent the degree of toxicity, because a thin layer of wax surrounding the egg may act as an important barrier. In such a case the insecticide would first have to dissolve the wax before being able to act deleteriously upon the embryonic insect. Furthermore this layer of wax is highly variable—thinner or thicker according to the species and the age of the egg.

At present, the chemical aspects of insect control have jumped into prominence, and in its sensational appeal DDT:

(dichlorodiphenyltrichloroethane)

$$\overline{D} \qquad \overline{D} \qquad \overline{T}$$

has overshadowed much other work of importance which may ultimately prove to be of greater value. DDT will not automatically rid the world of noxious insects since we have already observed disquieting evidence of the development of resistance to it by some houseflies and mosquitoes. As yet no chemical discovered has completely solved an entomological problem.

Within the last few years the problem of insect control has been studied from a very different angle. Until now great faith has been placed in the use of surface sprays, baits, traps, and the like, but the newly developed insecticide OMPA:

(octamethyl pyrophosphoramide)

$$\overline{O} \ \overline{M} \quad \overline{P} \qquad \quad \overline{A}$$

can be absorbed by plants through the leaves, roots, or stems, according to the manner in which it is applied. The plant then becomes poisonous to certain insects, and principally to red spider mites. If applied to the upper leaves this compound does not move to the lower leaves, but if applied to the soil in a liquid form it is absorbed by the roots and moves to all parts of the plant. Tests on roses in greenhouses have given good control of both aphids and red spider mites. Considerable testing is still needed, however, before OMPA will be released for general use. Possible danger to man, when food plants are grown on OMPA-treated soil, seems to be the big stumbling block.

The entire matter of insect control is a most serious one. A general theory bases the control of a given insect upon the thesis that populations must be in a state of balance with their environment. Research workers have been led to conclude that such a balance is subject either to competition between the insects when seeking the things they require for existence, or competition between their natural enemies hunting for them. Another school of thought based upon results showing influence of temperature and humidity upon the rate of insect reproduction, development, etc., places emphasis upon physical control factors.

During the past thirty years there has been a growing realization of the importance of acquiring a better understanding of the processes which regulate the abundance of animal populations. As early as 1914 investigators sought to show that insect populations were controlled by natural enemies, especially parasites. In addition to insect parasites, the agencies of a biological nature would include the total activities of bacterial, fungal, and other diseases, insectivorous birds, and predators. However, in order to protect his interests, man has found it necessary to devise additional means of combating insects. This he does by means of artificial control which may take many forms: quarantine; biological control; cultural and management control—the planting of resistant crops, crop rotation, clean cultivation, specific times of planting and harvesting; mechanical control—traps, handpicking, and mechanical barriers; physical control—electricity and heating of food in storage plants; and chemical control—stomach poisons, contact poisons, fumigants, repellents, and residuals. But of greatest importance are the steps taken by our Federal government to prevent the entry of foreign species of insects within the borders of this country. The continental United States is under the protection of Federal foreign-plant quarantines, Federal domestic-plant quarantines, and some hundred or more State plant quarantines. The domestic quarantines are directed against insects or diseases that are already in this country, but not in all parts of it, and their function is to prevent or delay the spread. In other words, quarantine is maintained as an inner defense (between states) and as an outer defense (against other countries).

Obviously, insects need food upon which to live and grow. The need for such control methods shows to what extent man has made this food-getting easier for the insects. One of the greatest contributions to the insects' food supply came with man's cultivation and concentration of food crops. Then as man became more gregarious he made it easier for ectoparasites, such as fleas and lice, to obtain their meal of blood—not only from him but also from the animals he domesticated. As a corollary of their increase there resulted insect-borne diseases. As if these factors were not enough, in the last fifty years man has also achieved new heights in methods of inadvertently transplanting insects from one state to another, and even from one continent to another by means of rapid transportation—by automobile, by rail, by sea, and by air. Thus man's progress lends a helping hand to the increase and dissemination of insects, toward the eradication of which he then expends time, energy, and money. Truly, it will be a never-ending cycle, although a balance eventually may be achieved by means of proper control.

Probably no other field in the range of biological endeavor, except medicine and bacteriology, offers so much promise to the young biologist today. Investigators of every sort are needed, as are field men to put into effect their recommendations. In addition to teaching, research, extension and regulatory work in federal or state agencies, the field has more recently expanded into legal entomology, photography, designs of insect origins, and into manufacturing—especially the chemical industries. More entomologically trained men and women will enable us better to control some insects and to receive more fully the benefits that others can give.

The more we learn about insects the better equipped we will be to deal with them under various conditions. Through increased studies we will be in a more favorable position to effect this balance between man, on the one hand, wanting the crops that he produces and uses for food, clothing, and shelter, and insects, on the other hand, feeding upon these things—crops, woolens, house timbers, and furniture.

Control, then, to a large extent, rests in the reduction of the ravages of pests and of destroyers of crops, and in the increased utilization of the insects that are useful to man. Intimate knowledge is the only means by which man can hope to minimize the competitive activity of insects as they affect his everyday living.

Bibliography

ALDRICH, J. M.   Flies of the Leptid Genus *Atherix* Used as Food by the California Indians. *Entomological News*, XXIII (April, 1912), pp. 159–163.

——————— Larvae of a Saturnid Moth Used as Food by California Indians. *Journal New York Entomological Society*, XX (March, 1912), pp. 28–31.

ALLARD, HARRY A.   Our Insect Instrumentalists. *Annual Report Smithsonian Institution*, 1928. Pub. 2981, U.S. Printing Office, Washington, D.C.: 1929. Pp. 563–591.

ANDREWS, ROY CHAPMAN.   Wings Win. *Natural History*, XL (October, 1937), no. 3, pp. 559–565.

ATKINS, E. LAURENCE JR.   Mimicry between the Drone-fly *Eristalis tenax* (L.) and the Honeybee, *Apis mellifera* (L.): Its Significance in Ancient Mythology and Present Day Thought. *Annals of Entomological Society of America*, XLI (September, 1948), no. 3, pp. 387–392.

BATCHELOR, JOHN.   Items of Ainu Folklore. *Journal American Folklore*, VII (January–March, 1894), no. 24, pp. 15–44.

BEAUCHAMP, WILLIAM MARTIN.   The Great Mosquito. *Journal American Folklore*, II (October–December, 1889), no. 7, p. 284.

BECK, BODAG FELIX.   *Honey and Health.*   New York: R. M. McBride and Co., 1938. Pp. 1–272.

BERGEN, FANNY D.   Current Superstitions. *Memoirs American Folklore Society*, IV (1896), pp. 55–130.

——————— Animal and Plant Lore. *Memoirs American Folklore Society*, VII (1899), pp. 11–95.

BIRKELAND, JORGEN.   *Microbiology and Man.*   New York: F. S. Crofts and Co., 1942. Pp. x + 478.

BLITZSTEIN, MADELIN.   The Stamp Collectors Zoo. *Travel*, LXXXV (June, 1945), no. 2, pp. 8–10.

BOAS, FRANZ. Current Beliefs of the Kwakiutl Indians. *Journal American Folklore*, XLV (April–June, 1932), no. 176, pp. 177–260.

BODENHEIMER, F. S. *Insects as Human Food.* The Hague: Dr. W. Junk, 1951. Pp. 1–352.

BOURKE, JOHN G. Popular Superstitions of the Rio Grande. *Journal American Folklore*, VII (April–June, 1894), no. 25, pp. 119–146.

BRICKELL, BIG JOHN. *The Natural History of North Carolina.* Dublin: Printed for the Author, MDCCXLIII (1743). Pp. xv + 408.

BRISTOWE, W. S. Insects and other Invertebrates for Human Consumption in Siam. *Transactions Entomological Society London*, LXXX (Part II), 1932, pp. 387–404.

BRODY, SAMUEL. Science and Dietary Wisdom. *Scientific Monthly*, LXI (September, 1945), no. 3, pp. 213–225.

BROMLEY, STANLEY W. The Last Few Years. *Journal New York Entomological Society*, LV (September, 1947), no. 3, p. 207.

BROWN, IRENE. Sonification in Insects. *Bios*, XXII (May, 1951), no. 2, pp. 105–111.

BRUES, CHARLES T. *Insect Dietary.* Cambridge Massachusetts: Harvard University Press, 1946. Pp. xxi + 466.

BRUGGER, A. T. The Deathhead Moth. *Gleanings in Bee Culture*, LXXIV (November, 1946), no. 11, pp. 603–651.

BUSVINE, JAMES. *Insects and Hygiene.* London: Methuen and Company Limited, 1951. Pp. xiv + 482.

CAMPBELL, J. M. Honey Superstitions. *American Anthropologist*, IX (January, 1896), no. 1, p. 13.

CHRISTY, ROBERT. *Proverbs, Maxims and Phrases of All Ages.* New York: Knickerbocker Press, 1888. Vol. I, pp. 1–655; vol. II, pp. 1–602.

CLARK, AUSTIN H. Some Observations on Butterfly Migrations. *Scientific Monthly*, XXXII (February, 1931), no. 2, pp. 150–155.

CLEVELAND, L. R. The Feeding Habit of Termite Castes and its Relation to their Intestinal Flagellates. *Biological Bulletin*, XLVIII (May, 1925), no. 5, pp. 295–306.

COMSTOCK, JOHN HENRY. *Introduction to Entomology.* Ithaca, New York: The Comstock Publishing Company, Inc., 1933. Pp. xix + 1044.

CORRINGTON, JULIAN D. Under the Microscope. *Nature Magazine*, XXXIX (1946), no. 4, pp. 221–224.

COWAN, FRANK. *Curious Facts in the History of Insects.* Philadelphia: Lippincott & Co., 1865. Pp. xvi + 396.

COWAN, JOHN. Honey-Making Ants. *Nature and Culture*, IV (May, 1912), no. 6, pp. 22–24.

CURTIS, NATALIE. *The Indian Book.* New York and London: Harper and Brothers Publishers, 1907. Pp. xxi + 573.

CUSHING, FRANK HAMILTON. The Origin Myth from Oraibi. *Journal American Folklore,* XXXVI (April–June, 1923), no. 140, pp. 163–170.

DAVIS, HENRY C. Negro Folklore in South Carolina. *Journal American Folklore,* XXVII (July–September, 1914), no. 105, pp. 241–254.

DOLBEAR, A. E. The Cricket as a Thermometer. *American Naturalist,* XXXI (November, 1897), no. 371, pp. 970–971.

DuBois, CONSTANCE G. The Mythology of the Dieguefios. *Journal American Folklore,* XIV (July–September, 1901), no. 54, pp. 181–185.

DUNCAN, CARL D. and PICKWELL, GAYLE. *The World of Insects.* New York and London: McGraw-Hill Book Company, Inc., 1939. Pp. ix + 409.

ECKERT, J. E. Beekeeping in California. *California Agriculture Extension Service, Circular 100.* College of Agriculture, University California, 1947. Pp. 3–95.

ELWIN, VERRIER A. Honey Festival. *Man in India,* XXIV (June, 1944), no. 2, pp. 85–88.

EMERSON, ALFRED E. Termite Architecture. *Natural History,* XXXIX (April, 1947), no. 4, pp. 242–248.

———— The Termite Problem. *Natural History,* XXXIX (April, 1947), no. 4, pp. 249–254.

ESSEX, HIRAM E. Certain Animal Venoms and their Physiologic Action. *Physiological Review,* XXV (January, 1945), no. 1, pp. 148–170.

ESSIG, E. O. *College Entomology.* New York: Macmillan, 1942. Pp. vii + 900.

———— The Value of Insects to the California Indians. *Scientific Monthly,* XXXVIII (January, 1934), no. 2, pp. 181–186.

FAGAN, MARGARET M. The Uses of Insect Galls. *The American Naturalist,* LII (February–March, 1918), no. 614, pp. 155–176.

FAULKNER, PEARL. Insects in English Poetry. *Scientific Monthly,* XXXIII (August, 1931), no. 2, pp. 148–163.

FEWKES, JESSE WALTER J. The Butterfly in Hopi Myth and Ritual. *American Anthropologist,* new series XII (October–December, 1910), no. 4, pp. 576–594.

Fogel, Edwin M. *Beliefs and Superstitions of the Pennsylvania Germans.* Americana Germanica Press, 1915. Pp. iv + 387.

FROST, S. W. *General Entomology.* New York and London: McGraw Hill Book Co. Inc., 1942. Pp. x + 524.

GARRETT, ROBERT MAX. Notes and Queries. *Journal American Folklore,* XXXIV (October–December, 1921), no. 134, p. 399.

GLICK, P. A.   The Distribution of Insects, Spiders and Mites in the Air. U.S. Dept. of Agriculture *Technical Bulletin* 673 (1939) pp. 1–150.

GRINNELL, GEORGE BIRD.   The Butterfly and the Spider Among the Blackfeet. *American Anthropologist,* new series, I (1899), pp. 194–196.

GROUT, ROY A.   Increased Profits from Wax Production. *American Bee Journal,* LXXXVII (May, 1947), no. 4, pp. 220–221.

GUDGER, EUGENE W.   Stitching Wounds with the Mandibles of Ants and Beetles. *Journal American Medical Association,* LXXXIV (1925), no. 24, pp. 1861–1864.

GUYTON, F. E.   Bee Sting Therapy for Arthritis and Neuritis. *Journal Economic Entomology,* XL (August, 1947), no. 4, pp. 469–472.

HALLMAN, MALCOLM SCOTT.   The Story of Honey Bees. *Bios,* XXII (October, 1951), no. 3, pp. 198–208.

HAMBLETON, JAMES I.   The Indispensable Honey Bee. *Annual Report of the Smithsonian Institution,* 1945.   Publication 2981, United States Government Printing Office, Washington, D.C.: 1946, pp. 293–304.

HANDSCHIN, E.   The Silkworm or *Bombyx mori* Linne.   *Ciba Review,* LIII (November, 1946), pp. 1902–1907.

HEARN, LAFCADIO.   *In Ghostly Japan.*   London: Samson Low, Marston and Co., 1899.   Pp. 1–241.

HERMS, WILLIAM B.   *Medical Entomology.*   New York: Macmillan Company, 3rd edition, 1939.   Pp. xix + 582.

HERSKOVITS, MELVILLE J.   Trinidad Proverbs. *Journal American Folklore,* LVIII (July–September, 1945), no. 229, pp. 195–207.

HESS, LILO.   The Jump in the Jumping Bean. *Nature Magazine,* XXXVIII (November, 1945), no. 9, pp. 473–475.

HEWLETT, JOHN.   Weaving the Loom of Life. *Travel,* LXXXV (June, 1945), no. 2, pp. 22–26.

HINMAN, E. H.   The Use of Insects and Other Arthropods in Medicine. *Journal Tropical Medicine and Hygiene,* XXXVI (May, 1933), no. 9, pp. 128–134.

HODGE, C. F.   How You Can Make Your Home, Town or City Flyless. *Nature and Culture,* III (July and August, 1911), nos. 2 and 3, pp. 9–23.

HOLBROOK, FLORENCE.   *The Book of Nature Myths.*   Boston, New York, Chicago: Houghton Mifflin Company, 1902.   Pp. 1 + 215.

HOLLAND, HENRIETTA.   Following the Sun with Honey Bees. *Frontiers,* IX (June, 1945), no. 5, pp. 151–153.

HOWARD, L. O.   *The Insect Menace.*   New York: The Century Company, 1937.   Pp. xv + 347.

HUGGINS, MABEL IRENE.   Cicada, Tortoise, Dove, Hare, Deer and Crane in Chinese Symbolism. *Nature Magazine*, XLI (February, 1948), no. 2, pp. 93–96.

INWARDS, RICHARD. *Weather-Lore* (A Collection of Proverbs, Sayings and Rules Concerning the Weather). New York: Harper Brothers, 1898. Pp. xii + 233.

JAEGER, ELLSWORTH. The Making of the Milky Way. *Hobbies*, XXVIII (October, 1947), no. 1, p. 13.

JANAKIRAMAN, A. T., and GURURAJAN, N. H. Silkworm Gut Industry. *Journal Scientific and Industrial Research*, III (February, 1945), no. 8, pp. 355–358.

JONES, W. RAY. Honey Poisoning. *Gleanings in Bee Culture*, LXXV (February, 1947), no. 2, pp. 76–77.

KARSTEN, RAFAEL. *The Civilization of the South American Indian*. New York: Alfred A. Knopf, 1926. Pp. xxxii + 540.

KELLOG, CLAUDE R. Beekeeping in Mexican Villages. *American Bee Journal*, LXXXV (October, 1945), no. 10, pp. 356–357.

KIRKALDY, G. W. An Economic Use for Waterbugs. *Entomological Monthly Magazine*, IX (June, 1898), no. 2, pp. 173–175.

KNAGGS, NELSON S. *Adventures in Man's First Plastic*. New York: Reinhold Publishing Corporation, 1947. Pp. xiv + 329.

LANGSTROTH, LORENZO L. *The Hive and the Honey Bee*. Illinois: Dadant and Sons, 1904. Pp. xv + 521.

LAUDERMILK, JERRY. Indians Made Their Own Dyes. *Desert Magazine*, VIII (March, 1945), no. 5, pp. 20–23.

LAUFER, BERTHOLD. *Insect Musicians and Cricket Champions of China*. Chicago: Field Museum of Natural History, 1927. Leaflet 22, pp. 1–27.

LEGGETT, WILLIAM F. *Ancient and Medieval Dyes*. Chemical Publishing Company, Incorporated, 1944. Pp. vi + 95.

LINN, ELIZABETH. Bee Venom as a Medicine. *Frontiers*, XIII (February, 1949), no. 3, pp. 76–78.

LINTNER, V. A. Habits of the Psocidae. *New York State Entomologist*, Second Annual Report, 1885. Pp. xiv + 221.

LORD, F. A. Australian Moth is World's Largest. *Journal Entomology and Zoology*, XL (September, 1948), no. 3, pp. 45–46.

MACARTHUR, W. P. Old Time Typhus in Britain. *Transactions Royal Society of Tropical Medicine and Hygiene*, XX (April, 1927), pp. 487–503.

MANN, WILLIAM M. Stalking Ants, Savage and Civilized. *National Geographic Magazine*, LXVI (August, 1934), no. 2, pp. 171–192.

MARTIN, SARAH. Pious-Looking Monster of the Insect World—Praying Monster. *Frontiers*, IX (April, 1945), no. 4, pp. 126–127.

McATEE, W. L. Popular Names of Gyrinidae. *Journal New York Entomological Society*, LV (September, 1947), no. 3, pp. 205–209.

MENKE, HERMAN L. Apple Pollination in Washington State. *Gleanings in Bee Culture*, LXXIX (April, 1951), no. 4, pp. 201–205.

METCALF, C. L., and FLINT, W. P. *Destructive and Useful Insects.* New York, London: McGraw-Hill Company, 1939. Pp. xvi + 981.

MONTGOMERY, B. E. Insect Stamps. *Entomological News*, XLVIII (July, 1937), no. 7, pp. 184–186.

MOONEY, JAMES. *Myths of the Cherokee.* Bureau of American Ethnology, 19th Annual Report, 1897–1898. Washington, D.C.: United States Government Printing Office, 1900. Pp. 3–548.

MUNRO, AENEAS. *The Locust Plague and its Suppression.* London: John Murray, 1900. Pp. xvi + 365.

NABOUR, ROBERT K. The Derivation of Hymenoptera. *Annals Entomological Society of America*, XXXVIII (December, 1945), no. 4, p. 457.

OBERMAIER, HUGO. *Fossil Man in Spain.* New Haven: Published for the Hispanic Society of America by the Yale University Press, 1924. Pp. xxviii + 495.

PEATTIE, DONALD CULROSS. Honey—Golden Wonder. *Nature Magazine*, XLII (April, 1949), no. 4, p. 163.

PELLET, FRANK C. The Honey Bee—Source of the World's Most Famous Food. *Bios*, XV (May, 1944), no. 2, pp. 51–65.

PETERSON, HAROLD R. The Value of the Honeybee in Pollinating Crops. *American Bee Journal*, LXXXV (November, 1945), no. 11, p. 403.

PETRIE, W. M. FLINDERS. *Scarabs and Cylinders with Names.* London: School of Archeology in Egypt and Constable and Company, Limited, and Bernard Quaritch, 1917. Pp. viii + 46, plates I—LXXIII.

PETTIT, LINCOLN C. A Roach is Born. *Fauna*, VI (June, 1944), no. 2, pp. 50–52.

PRICE, SADIE F. Kentucky Folklore. *Journal American Folklore*, XIV (January–March, 1901), no. 52, pp. 30–38.

PUCKETT, Newbell N. *Folk Beliefs of the Southern Negro.* University of North Carolina Press, 1926. Pp. xiv + 644.

RADBILL, SAMUEL X. Child Hygiene Among the Indians. *Texas Reports on Biology and Medicine*, III (Winter, 1945), no. 4, pp. 419–512.

RANDOLPH, VANCE. Folk Belief in the Ozark Mountains. *Journal American Folklore*, XL (January–March, 1927), no. 155, pp. 78–93.

———— Ozark Superstitions. *Journal American Folklore*, XLVI (January–March, 1933), no. 179, pp. 3–21.

RANSOME, HILDA M. *The Sacred Bee.* Boston and New York: Houghton-Mifflin Company, 1937. Pp. 1–308.

ROBERTS, HILDA. Louisiana Superstitions. *Journal American Folklore,* XL (April–June, 1927), no. 156, pp. 144–208.

ROTH, WALTER E. An Inquiry into Animism and Folklore of the Guiana Indians. *Thirtieth Annual Report Bureau of American Ethnology,* 1913, pp. 117–386.

SCHMEIDER, R. G. On Directing the Flight of Bees. *Entomological News,* LVII (January, 1946), no. 1, pp. 16–19.

SCHWARZ, A. Silk Reels and Silk Mills. *Ciba Review,* LIX (August, 1947), pp. 2145–2153.

SCHWARZ, HERBERT F. The Wax of Stingless Bees (Meliponidae) and the uses to which it has been put. *Journal New York Entomological Society,* LIII (June, 1945), no. 2, pp. 137–144.

SIAN-TEK, LIM. *More Folk Tales from China.* New York: The John Day Company, 1948. Pp. 1–160.

SMILEY, PORTIA. Folklore from Virginia, South Carolina, Georgia, Alabama and Florida. *Journal American Folklore,* XXXII (July–September, 1919), pp. 357–383.

STAFFORD, A. O. The Mind of the African Negro as Reflected in his Proverbs. *Journal Negro History,* I (January, 1916), no. 1, pp. 42–48.

SWANTON, J. R. Religious Beliefs and Medical Practices of Creek Indians. Forty-Second Annual Report, *Bureau of Ethnology,* 1924–25. United States Printing Office, 1928, pp. 25–388.

TEALE, EDWIN WAY. Knothole Cavern. *Natural History,* L (October, 1942), no. 3, pp. 153–157.

TEIT, JAMES A. Tahltan Tales. *Journal American Folklore,* XXXII (April–June, 1919), no. 124, pp. 198–250.

THOMAS, DANIEL and BLAYNEY, LUCY. *Kentucky Superstitions.* Princeton University Press, 1920. Pp. viii + 334.

TORRE-BUENO, J. R. DE LA. Why Not Eat Insects? *Bulletin Brooklyn Entomological Society,* XXXIX (October, 1944), no. 4, pp. 122–131.

————— A Bibliographic Note on Aquatic Hemiptera Used as Food in Mexico. *Bulletin Brooklyn Entomological Society,* XXXVII (December, 1942), no. 5, pp. 168–169.

TREVELYAN, MARIE. *Folklore and Folk Stories of Wales.* London: Elliot Stock, 1909. Pp. xiii + 348.

VOSBURGH, FREDERICK G. Torchbearers of the Twilight. *National Geographic Magazine,* XCIX (May, 1951), no. 5, pp. 697–704.

WEISS, HARRY B. Cockroaches for Tetanus and Indigestion. *Journal*

New York Entomological Society, XXXIII (December, 1925), no. 4, p. 232

Weiss, Harry B. Insects and Witchcraft. *Journal New York Entomological Society,* XXXVIII (June, 1930), no. 2, pp. 127–133.

———— Some Early Entomological Ideas and Practices in America. *Journal New York Entomological Society,* LIII (December, 1945), no. 4, pp. 301–308.

———— An Old Use for Cockroaches. *Journal New York Entomological Society,* LIV (June, 1946), no. 2, p. 166.

Wheeler, William Morton. *Ants, their structure, development and behaviour.* New York: Columbia University Press, 1910. Pp. ix + 664.

Whitney, Annie W. and Bullock, Caroline C. Folk-lore from Maryland. *Memoirs American Folklore Society,* XVIII (1925), p. 1–239.

Wood, Horatio C. and Osal, Arthur. *The Dispensatory of the United States of America.* New York: J. B. Lippincott and Company, 23rd Edition, 1943, pp. 251–254.

Yancey, P. H. Origins from Mythology of Biological Names and Terms. *Bios,* XVI (March, 1945), no. 1, pp. 7–9.

———— *Bios,* XVI (May, 1945), no. 2, pp. 73–88.

Young, Egerton, R. *Algonquin Indian Tales.* New York: Eaton and Mains, 1903. Pp. 1–258.

Index